Introduction to Audio Signal Processing

Warren L. G. Koontz

Introduction to Audio Signal Processing

Warren L. G. Koontz

 RIT PRESS

Rochester, New York

Introduction to Audio Signal Processing
©2016 Warren L.G. Koontz and Rochester Institute of Technology

Distributed by:

RIT Press
90 Lomb Memorial Drive
Rochester, New York 14623
http://ritpress.rit.edu

Book design by Warren L. G. Koontz
Cover design by Marnie Soom

Printed in the U.S.A.

ISBN 978-1-939125-41-5 (print)
ISBN 978-1-939125-42-2 (ebook)

Library of Congress Cataloging-in-Publication Data

Name: Koontz, Warren L. G., author.

Title: Introduction to audio signal processing / Warren L.G. Koontz

Description: Rochester, New York: RIT Press, [2016] | Includes bibliographical references and index.

Identifiers: LCCN 2016046464 (print) | LCCN 2016049079 (ebook) | ISBN 9781939125415 (softcover : alk. paper) | ISBN 9781939125422 (ebook)

Subjects: LCSH: Sound – Recording and reproducing – Digital techniques. | Signal processing – Digital techniques.

Classification: LCC TK7881.4. K66 2016 (print) | LCC TK7881.4 (ebook) | DDC 621.382/2 – dc23

LC record available at https://lccn.loc.gov/2016046464

For Rebecca, Andrew, Daniel, and Bowen

Contents

List of Figures

List of Tables

Nomenclature

μPa	micro-pascal
CD	compact disk
DFT	discrete Fourier transform
DTFS	discrete-time Fourier series
DTFT	discrete-time Fourier transform
FDN	feedback delay network
FFT	fast Fourier transform
FIR	finite impulse response
GUI	graphical user interface
Hz	hertz
IDFT	inverse DFT
IIR	infinite impulse response
kHz	kilohertz
LPC	linear predictive coding
LTIS	linear time-invariant systems
MDCT	modified discrete cosine transform
MPN	multiport element network
Pa	pascal
PCM	pulse-code modulation
PSD	power spectral density
RMS	root mean squared
SPL	sound pressure level
STFT	short-time Fourier transform

Chapter 1

Introduction

The phrase *audio engineering* is used to describe a wide variety of professional activities, including the application of artistic as well as technical skills and knowledge. This book is aimed primarily at the technical side of the profession and is intended for engineering students who desire a concentration in the application of engineering methodology, in particular audio signal processing, to the production and refinement of audio material.

When we think of audio engineering we may imagine an engineer working in a large room and surrounded by a vast array of electronic equipment. While this is often the case for professional audio engineers, it is now possible and quite common for an artist to record and process audio content on a laptop computer with appropriate software and interface devices. Small and affordable devices are available to connect microphones and musical instruments to a personal computer via a standard digital interface. A number of software products are available to support multitrack recording and mixing, adding effects, and producing a finished audio product in any of several common digital formats. This book describes basic signal-processing tools and algorithms that are applied in the recording and production of audio content. In addition it provides examples and exercises related to straightforward implementations of the algorithms that can be run on any device that supports MATLAB.

The initial chapters of the book provide an overview of audio signals and processing systems in both the analog and digital domains. This material, which may be review for some students, establishes notation and develops analysis tools for subsequent application. The later chapters cover the major applications of these tools in audio signal processing, including filtering and equalization, effect generation, and audio compression. The mathematical level should be comfortable for both engineering and engineering technology undergraduates. Although there is some calculus and a differential equation or two, the emphasis is on digital methods in which derivatives become differences and integrals become sums.

The book makes considerable use of MATLAB, and it is recommended that any course based on this book include exercises using MATLAB or a similar tool so that students can implement some of the concepts, especially in the digital arena. Several chapters of this book include recommended MATLAB exercises.

1

The following is an outline of the remaining chapters of this book:

Chapter 2 Analog Audio Signals

- Description of sound in terms of acoustic pressure. Measures of acoustic pressure.
- Basic analog signals, including sinusoidal signals, periodic signals, and random (noise) signals. Fourier analysis of analog signals.
- Analog signal processing. Introduction to and characterization of linear time-invariant systems.

Chapter 3 Digital Coding of Sound

- Conversion of an analog signal to digital by means of sampling and quantization.
- The sampling process. Sampling theory and the Nyquist criterion. Alias signals.
- Linear and nonlinear quantization. Quantizing error.

Chapter 4 Digital Audio Signal Processing

- Basic digital signals, including impulse, exponential, and periodic signals.
- Characterization of digital linear time-invariant systems. Impulse response, frequency response, and transfer function. The z-transform.
- Fourier analysis of digital signals and systems. Discrete-time Fourier series and transform.

Chapter 5 Spectral Analysis of Audio Signals

- Frequency domain view of audio signals.
- Short-time Fourier transform and spectrogram analysis.

Chapter 6 Frequency-Shaping Filters

- Basic filter types, including low-pass, high-pass, band-pass/stop, peak, and shelf filters.
- Overview of filter specification and design.
- Equalizer design and implementation.
- Audio source model filters.

Chapter 7 Audio Effect Generation

- Fading, flanger, chorus, and wah-wah effects.
- Dynamic range control.
- Tempo and pitch variation.
- Noise reduction.

Chapter 8 Reverberation

- Reverberation effect based on measured impulse response.

- Building blocks for creating reverberation effect.

- Reverberation effect based on state-space filters and multiport elements.

Chapter 9 Audio Compression

- MPEG (Motion Picture Experts Group) approach to audio compression.

- Polyphase analysis and synthesis filters.

- Psychoacoustic model of the listener.

Chapter 2

Analog Audio Signals

If you pluck a string on an acoustic guitar, the string will vibrate rapidly for at least a few seconds. Since the string is anchored to the guitar at the bridge, the body of the guitar, especially the soundboard, will vibrate along with the string. The air around the guitar is displaced by these vibrations, resulting in small variations in air pressure that in turn affect more of the air around the guitar, so that in a short time the variations are occurring at some distance from the guitar. Upon reaching a healthy human ear, the variations in air pressure create vibrations in the eardrum that are processed by the inner ear into electrical signals that are passed on to the brain and interpreted as sound.

What we have described here is a simple *audio system* consisting of three components:

Source

> In this example the source is the acoustic guitar. In general an acoustic source is a mechanism that sets the surrounding medium in motion. Mechanisms include mechanical vibration (guitar strings and soundboard, loudspeaker cone, etc.), explosion (sudden release of gas by burst balloon, gunshot, etc.), and turbulence (forcing air through a small aperture). The human voice uses many of these mechanisms to produce the vast variety of sounds of spoken language.

Medium

> A medium is necessary to carry the sound away from the source – sound cannot exist in a vacuum. The most common medium in human experience is the air around us, but many media are possible, including liquid and solid media and gas. As stated above, the source sets the medium in motion, and this motion spreads away from the source as an *acoustic wave*. Acoustic waves are analogous to the waves that form in still water when it disturbed by, for example, a tossed stone.

Receiver

> Although the combination of a source and a medium is sufficient to create sound, it is more interesting when the system includes a human listener (or other hearing animal), a recording device, or some other acoustic receiver. A receiver usually includes a membrane or other structure that is set in motion by the sound wave and a mechanism to convert this motion into an electrical

4

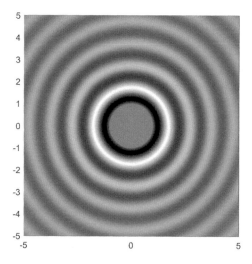

Figure 2.1: Illustration of a sound wave.

(usually) signal. In the case of a human listener, the membrane is the eardrum and the inner ear creates electrical impulses that are carried by the nervous system to the brain.

Figure 2.1 is a rough, two-dimensional illustration of an acoustic wave generated by a hypothetical omnidirectional source (e.g., a vibrating sphere) in an air medium. The alternating dark and light shading represents variation in the local air pressure caused by the sound source. In the dark areas the air pressure is above the normal atmospheric level, and in the light areas the air pressure is below the normal atmospheric level. The high- and low-pressure areas are called *compressions* and *rarefactions*, respectively. The figure represents a moment in time. In an animated version of the figure,[1] the compression and rarefaction waves propagate away from the source. Thus, in the presence of sound, air pressure is varying (rapidly!) with both time and location.

2.1   Acoustic Pressure

An acoustic source disturbs the medium around it and causes properties of the medium to vary with time and location. If the medium is air, one of the affected properties is the air pressure, which we will measure in pascals (Pa), where $1\,\text{Pa} = 1\,\text{N/m}^2$. For now we will limit our discussion to the variation of pressure with time at some fixed point in space.

The total atmospheric pressure at a given point in the presence of sound can be modeled mathematically as

$$P(t) = p(t) + P_0 \tag{2.1}$$

---

[1]See, for example, `http://whatmusicreallyis.com/research/cymatics/`

where $P(t)$ is the total pressure, $p(t)$ is the *acoustic pressure* caused by an acoustic wave, and P_0 is the normal atmospheric pressure. The notation indicates the time dependence of the total pressure and the acoustic pressure. The normal atmospheric pressure is treated as a constant, since it varies much more slowly than the acoustic pressure. The normal atmospheric pressure P_0 is about 100 000 Pa at sea level. During a compression the total pressure is greater than P_0 and $p(t)$ is positive. During a rarefaction the total pressure is less than P_0 and $p(t)$ is negative. Except for a relatively small number of basic sounds, such as pure tones, we cannot completely specify $p(t)$ with a simple mathematical expression using common functions. We can, however, define some useful overall measures of $p(t)$, such as the RMS (root mean squared) amplitude.

The RMS amplitude of the acoustic pressure is given by

$$p_{\text{rms}} = \sqrt{\frac{1}{T} \int_0^T p^2(t)dt} \tag{2.2}$$

where T is a suitable time-averaging interval. If $p(t)$ is measured in pascals, then p_{rms} is also in pascals. The RMS amplitude of acoustic pressure, which is related to the perceived loudness of the sound, is much smaller than P_0 and is usually measured in micro-pascals (μPa).

Sound pressure level (SPL) is a more common measure of acoustic pressure. SPL is a logarithmic measure given by

$$\text{SPL} = 20 \log_{10} \left(\frac{p_{\text{rms}}}{p_{\text{ref}}} \right) \tag{2.3}$$

where p_{ref} is the reference level, which is set at 20 μPa (the minimum level that a human can hear). The units of SPL are decibels SPL (dB SPL). The inverse formula to convert SPL to acoustic pressure is

$$p_{\text{rms}} = p_{\text{ref}} 10^{\text{SPL}/20} \tag{2.4}$$

Example 2.1.1. The RMS acoustic pressure of a certain sound is 100 μPa. Calculate the corresponding SPL.

Solution

$$\text{SPL} = 20 \log_{10} \left(\frac{100}{20} \right)$$
$$= 13.98 \text{ dB SPL}$$

Table 2.1 lists the RMS and SPL measures of acoustic pressure for a variety of sounds. Table 2.1 shows that whereas the RMS level varies by orders of magnitude from the quietest to the loudest sounds, dB SPL increases more or less linearly. Also, dB SPL appears to be more closely related to human perception of loudness.

The auditory system responds to acoustic pressure to create the experience of hearing. This means that the acoustic pressure function $p(t)$ contains all of the information needed about the sound that reaches the listener's ear. Moreover, any function of the form $x(t) = Kp(t)$, where K is a constant scale factor, contains the same information. For example, a microphone converts acoustic pressure to

Description	RMS Level (Pa)	dB SPL
Threshold of hearing	0.00002	0
Empty recording studio	0.0002	20
Average home	0.0063	50
Vacuum cleaner @ 1 m	0.063	70
Diesel truck @ 10 m	0.63	90
Chain saw @ 1 m	6.3	110
Threshold of pain	63.0	130

Table 2.1: Acoustic pressure and dB SPL for various sounds.

an electrical voltage $v(t) = K_{mic}p(t)$. In this case the factor K_{mic} is called the *sensitivity* of the microphone and is measured in volts/pascal (V/Pa). With the help of an amplifier and a loudspeaker, the voltage $v(t)$ can, at least theoretically, reproduce the acoustic pressure function $p(t)$. In practice the reproduction will never be perfect, but with high-quality components it will be quite close.

We will refer to a function $x(t)$ that is derived from and can ultimately reproduce an acoustic pressure function as an *audio signal*. The domain of an audio signal, i.e., the set of possible values of $x(t)$, can be mechanical (e.g., displacement of a membrane or string). electrical (e.g., voltage or current), magnetic or simply numbers stored in a computer. A mechanism to convert an audio signal from one domain to another is sometimes called a *transducer*. Much of this book is about audio signals in the electrical or numerical domain. Nevertheless, we should keep in mind that, at least for now, we have to eventually produce an acoustic pressure function $p(t)$ for human consumption.

Figure 2.2a is a display of an audio signal showing the variation of amplitude (in arbitrary units for now) with time over a period of about 7.5 s. This is the time domain view of an audio signal, since time is the independent variable. Figure 2.2b shows a short segment of this audio signal illustrating a complex variation of the amplitude with time.

Before addressing realistic audio signals like this one, it is useful to examine some simpler and more fundamental waveforms such as pure tones and multiple tones. We will find later on that the simpler signals can tell us much about their complex relatives.

2.2 Basic Analog Signals

2.2.1 Sinusoidal Signals

The most basic audio signal is the pure tone, which is expressed mathematically as the sine function, i.e.,

$$x(t) = A\sin(2\pi ft + \phi) \tag{2.5}$$

where A is the peak amplitude (or just amplitude), f is the frequency in hertz (Hz), and ϕ is the phase in degrees or radians. For the time being, let the phase be zero degrees. Note that the independent variable t still represents time, which is in seconds when the frequency f is in hertz. Figure 2.3 illustrates this signal for $A = 5$ and $f = 1$ kHz. The pure tone is fairly rare in nature and is not very interesting

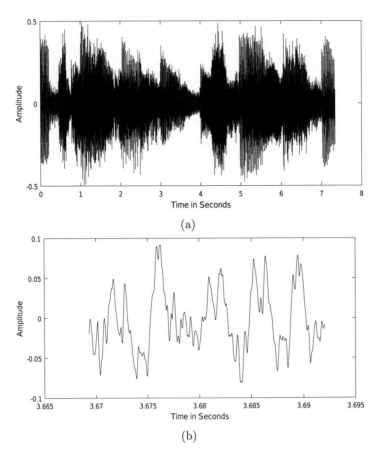

Figure 2.2: Example of an audio signal: (a) complete signal, (b) short segment of the signal.

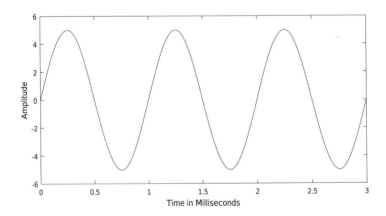

Figure 2.3: Sinusoidal audio signal.

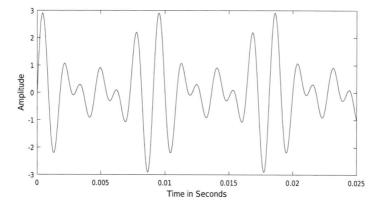

Figure 2.4: Simple major triad audio signal.

from a musical or communication point of view. However, it turns out to be a building block for more complex signals, as we will see later on. A reasonably pure tone can be generated by a tuning fork or an audio oscillator (an electronic device).

Note that the pure tone introduces the concept of frequency. As shown in Figure 2.3, the amplitude varies in repeating patterns or cycles. The time required to complete a cycle is known as the period (usually denoted T) and the frequency f is the inverse of the period, i.e.,

$$f = 1/T \tag{2.6}$$

If the period T is in seconds, then the frequency is in hertz, although frequency is sometimes expressed as cycles per second (1 cps = 1 Hz) or even inverse seconds (s^{-1}).

Humans perceive frequency as musical pitch, and a high pitch corresponds to a high frequency. For example, the musical note A above middle C has a standard frequency of 440 Hz.[2] The range of frequencies that a human can hear is limited – for a young person with normal hearing the range is from about 20 Hz to about 20 kHz. Perhaps for this reason, the term audio signal generally applies only to tones with frequencies in this range, and higher-frequency tones are referred to as *ultrasound*.

Pure tones with different amplitudes and frequencies can be combined to produce more complex audio signals. For example, we can construct a crude example of a major triad by summing three sinusoidal signals with frequencies in the ratio 4:5:6. If the amplitudes are all equal and the phases are all zero, this simplified triad can be expressed as

$$x(t) = \sin 2\pi f_0 t + \sin 2\pi (5 f_0 / 4) t + \sin 2\pi (6 f_0 / 4) t \tag{2.7}$$

Figure 2.4 illustrates a few cycles of this signal for $f_0 = 440$ Hz.

So far we have defined the pure tone using the sine function, but we can just as well use the cosine function. Moreover it is sometimes mathematically convenient to use the complex exponential function, i.e.,

$$x(t) = A e^{j(\omega t + \phi)} \tag{2.8}$$

---

[2]At least in some countries.

where $\omega = 2\pi f$ is the frequency in *radians per second* and $j = \sqrt{-1}$. The complex exponential function is related to the cosine and sine functions by Euler's identity:

$$e^{j\theta} = \cos\theta + j\sin\theta \tag{2.9}$$

Thus, if $x(t)$ is given by Equation (2.8), then the real and imaginary parts of $x(t)$ are given by

$$\Re[x(t)] = A\cos(\omega t + \phi)$$
$$\Im[x(t)] = A\sin(\omega t + \phi) \tag{2.10}$$

2.2.2   Periodic Signals

Both the pure tone and the triad are examples of periodic signals in that they consist of a pattern that is continuously repeated. In general, a signal $x(t)$ is said to be periodic with period T if for all values of t

$$x(t - T) = x(t) \tag{2.11}$$

and T is the smallest value for which this is true. A periodic signal with period T can be represented by a Fourier series, i.e.,

$$x(t) = a_0 + \sum_{n=1}^{\infty}(a_n\cos 2\pi n f_0 t + b_n\sin 2\pi n f_0 t) \tag{2.12}$$

where $f_0 = 1/T$ and

$$a_0 = \frac{1}{T}\int_0^T x(t)dt$$

$$a_n = \frac{2}{T}\int_0^T x(t)\cos 2\pi n f_0 t dt$$

$$b_n = \frac{2}{T}\int_0^T x(t)\sin 2\pi n f_0 t dt \tag{2.13}$$

This means that a periodic signal is the summation of an infinite number of components, including a constant component and sinusoidal components (sine and cosine functions) at integer multiples of the fundamental frequency f_0. The frequency components for $n \geq 2$ are known as harmonics. This result is the source of the earlier claim that the sine wave is the building block of a large class of signals. The presence of both a sine and cosine function may be confusing, but it is simply equivalent to stating that each component may have, in addition to a different frequency, a different phase.

Although the formulas in Equation (2.13) look rather intimidating, they have already been evaluated for many periodic signals that crop up in various applications. Moreover, numerical methods are available to handle the less common or more complex signals. Note that the coefficient a_0 is the average value of $x(t)$ and is sometimes referred to as the DC component of the signal.

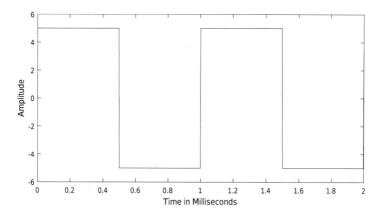

Figure 2.5: Square wave signal.

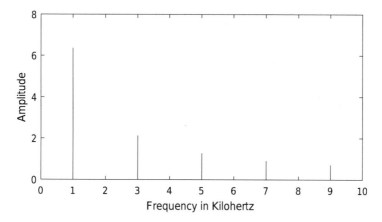

Figure 2.6: Amplitudes of the components of a square wave.

Example 2.2.1. Figure 2.5 illustrates a common periodic signal known as the square wave, in this case with a period of 1 ms and, therefore, a fundamental frequency of 1 kHz. The result of applying Equation 2.13 to this square wave is

$$a_n = 0 \tag{2.14}$$

$$b_n = \begin{cases} 0 & \text{if } n \text{ is even} \\ \dfrac{4A}{n\pi} & \text{if } n \text{ is odd} \end{cases} \tag{2.15}$$

where A is the amplitude of the square wave ($A = 5$ in this example). Thus, for this signal there is no DC component and no cosine components, and the sine components occur for only the fundamental frequency and the odd harmonics. The amplitudes of the components decrease with increasing frequency. Figure 2.6 is a plot of the amplitudes of the fundamental frequency component and the first four harmonics.

In general a periodic signal includes components at an infinite number of frequencies, all of which are integer multiples of the fundamental frequency f_0. This raises the question whether this kind of signal can be considered as an audio signal at all! The practical answer is yes, as long as the amplitudes of the high-frequency components are small compared with those of the audio frequency (i.e., less than 20 kHz) components. For example, the magnitude of the 19 kHz component of the 1 kHz square wave is 1/19 that of the 1 kHz fundamental component.

A more rigorous (but not necessarily standard) definition of an audio periodic signal can be obtained from consideration of the average signal power, which is given by

$$\bar{P} = \frac{K}{T} \int_0^T x^2(t)dt \tag{2.16}$$

where K is an appropriate factor to convert the square of the amplitude of $x(t)$ to watts (e.g., if $x(t)$ is electric current, then K is the associated resistance in ohms). For simplicity, and without much loss of generality, let $K = 1$. According to Parseval's theorem

$$\frac{1}{T} \int_0^T x^2(t)dt = a_0^2 + \frac{1}{2} \sum_{n=1}^{\infty}(a_n^2 + b_n^2) \tag{2.17}$$

Thus, the total average signal power is the sum of the average power of each component. An audio signal can now be defined as a signal with most of the power (e.g., 90%) is accounted for by components at frequencies below 20 kHz. For example, consider the square wave in Figure 2.5. Direct application of Equation (2.16) yields

$$\bar{P} = \frac{1}{T} \int_0^T x^2(t)dt = A^2 = 25 \tag{2.18}$$

Partial evaluation of Equation (2.17) shows that the first 20 components of the spectrum account for 98% of the power in a 1 kHz square wave. This result supports the claim that a 1 kHz square wave is an audio signal. In fact, if you "play" a 1 kHz square wave, it sounds like a high-pitched buzz.

Another example of a periodic signal corresponds to the sound generated by a vibrating mechanical element, such as stretched string, that is not subject to damping or other energy loss (e.g., a guitar string with infinite sustain).

Equation (2.12) is not the only form of the Fourier series. The complex exponential form given by the following pair of equations is also popular:

$$x(t) = \sum_{n=-\infty}^{\infty} c_n e^{j2\pi n f_0 t} \tag{2.19}$$

$$c_n = \frac{1}{T} \int_0^T x(t)e^{-j2\pi n f_0 t}dt \tag{2.20}$$

Application of Euler's identity shows that the coefficients for the two forms are related as follows:

$$\begin{aligned} a_n &= \Re(c_n) & n &= 0, 1, 2, \ldots \\ b_n &= -\Im(c_n) & n &= 1, 2, \ldots \end{aligned} \tag{2.21}$$

Note that c_n is defined for both positive and negative values of n as well as for $n = 0$. Note also that c_{-n} is simply the complex conjugate of c_n.

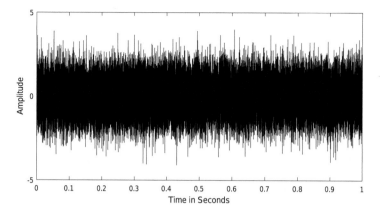

Figure 2.7: Audio signal from the sound of "s".

Figure 2.8: Linear time-invariant system.

2.2.3 Random Signals

Some signals appear almost chaotic in comparison with the signals we have considered so far. For example, human speech contains many sounds that are produced by forcing air through a constriction, creating turbulence. This results in an audio signal in which the amplitude varies in a seemingly random fashion. Figure 2.7 is an audio signal produced by the sound in English of the letter "s." The signal resembles so-called *white noise*, and even a close-up fails to show any kind of repeating pattern or regular structure.

Random signals can be described mathematically as *random processes*. A detailed discussion of random processes is beyond the scope of this book. However, we will return to this topic in our discussion of noise removal in Chapter 7.

2.3 Analog Signal Processing

It is often necessary to transform an audio signal in some way. For example, the audio signal produced by a microphone is far too weak to drive a loudspeaker and must be amplified to a sufficient power level. Later in this book we will discuss a number of ways an audio signal can be processed to improve its quality or to add desired effects. At this point, however, we will introduce the concept of a linear, time-invariant system (LTIS), which is the basis of many signal-processing systems.

Figure 2.8 illustrates an LTIS processing an input signal $x(t)$ and producing an output signal $y(t)$. An LTIS has the following two properties:

- Linearity – If input $x_1(t)$ produces output $y_1(t)$ and input $x_2(t)$ produces

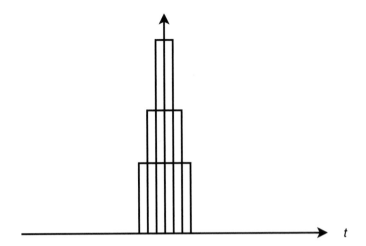

Figure 2.9: Impulse as the limit of a sequence of pulses.

output $y_2(t)$, then input $a_1x_1(t) + a_2x_2(t)$ produces output $a_1y_1(t) + a_2y_2(t)$.

- Time-invariance – If input $x(t)$ produces output $y(t)$, then input $x(t-T)$ produces output $y(t-T)$.

In the next two subsections we will present two models of an LTIS – one based on a function known as the *impulse response* and one based on a linear differential equation.

2.3.1   Impulse Response Model of an LTIS

We will now show that we can determine the output of an LTIS for any input signal $x(t)$ if we know the output of the LTIS for a particular input signal known as the *impulse function* $\delta(t)$.   Figure 2.9 shows three "pulse" signals – signals that are zero for all time except for an interval during which they have a constant nonzero amplitude. These pulses are part of a sequence of pulses with greater and greater amplitude and shorter and shorter duration. The vertical arrow represents the limit of this sequence – a very short pulse with a very large amplitude. The impulse function can be defined more precisely as

$$\delta(t) = 0, t \neq 0$$

$$\int_{-\infty}^{\infty} \delta(t)dt = 1 \tag{2.22}$$

Given this definition, it is fairly straightforward to show that for some signal $x(t)$

$$x(t) = \int_{-\infty}^{\infty} \delta(t-\tau)x(\tau)d\tau \tag{2.23}$$

Thus, the impulse function can be used to select the value of another function at a particular point in time.

The *impulse response* of a system, usually denoted $h(t)$, is the output of the system when the input is an impulse function, i.e., if $x(t) = \delta(t)$ then $y(t) = h(t)$. We can approximate the integral in Equation (2.23) with a summation

$$x(t) = \sum_{n=-\infty}^{\infty} \delta(t - n\Delta\tau)x(n\Delta\tau)\Delta\tau \qquad (2.24)$$

Since the system is both linear and time invariant, if the input is this summation then the output will be

$$y(t) = \sum_{n=-\infty}^{\infty} h(t - n\Delta\tau)x(n\Delta\tau)\Delta\tau \qquad (2.25)$$

This relation holds when we take the sum to the limiting integral so that

$$y(t) = \int_{-\infty}^{\infty} h(t - \tau)x(\tau)d\tau \qquad (2.26)$$

Equation (2.26) is an example of a *convolution integral* and is an important property of an LTIS. This equation proves our claim that given the impulse response of an LTIS, we can determine the response of the system to any input.

Example 2.3.1. An LTIS has an impulse response given by

$$h(t) = \omega_0 e^{-\omega_0 t}u(t)$$

where $u(t)$ is the *unit step function* defined by

$$u(t) = \begin{cases} 1 & t \geq 0 \\ 0 & t < 0 \end{cases}$$

and $\omega_0 > 0$. Determine the output of the system when the input is $x(t) = e^{j\omega t}$ (i.e., complex exponential form of a sinusoid). The frequency of the sinusoid ω is in radians/second ($\omega = 2\pi f$).

Solution Substituting the given information into Equation (2.26) we have

$$y(t) = \int_{-\infty}^{t} \omega_0 e^{-\omega_0(t-\tau)}e^{j\omega\tau}d\tau$$

Note that the upper limit of the integral is t rather than ∞, because $h(t) = 0$ for $t < 0$. This will be true for any LTIS that is physically realizable, since the output of a real system cannot depend on future inputs! The result of this rather straightforward integration is

$$y(t) = \frac{\omega_0 e^{j\omega t}}{j\omega + \omega_0}$$

Note that by Euler's identity the input signal in this example is the sum of a real part ($\cos \omega t$) and an imaginary part ($j \sin \omega t$). Thus, the output of this LTIS has a real part, which is the response to the real part of the input, and an imaginary part, which is the response to the imaginary part of the input. The response of this LTIS to the input $x(t) = \cos \omega t$ is therefore

$$y(t) = \Re \left\{ \frac{\omega_0 e^{j\omega t}}{j\omega + \omega_0} \right\}$$

$$= \omega_0 \frac{\omega_0 \cos \omega t + \omega \sin \omega t}{\omega^2 + \omega_0^2}$$

Equation (2.26) is often expressed in shorthand as

$$y(t) = h(t) * x(t) \tag{2.27}$$

The right-hand side of the equation is called the *convolution* of $h(t)$ and $x(t)$. Moreover, convolution is commutative, i.e.,

$$h(t) * x(t) = x(t) * h(t) \tag{2.28}$$

Let us now determine the output of a general LTIS when the input is $x(t) = e^{j\omega t}$. In this case the output $y(t)$ is given by

$$y(t) = \int_{-\infty}^{\infty} e^{j\omega(t-\tau)} h(\tau) d\tau$$

$$= e^{j\omega t} \int_{-\infty}^{\infty} e^{-j\omega \tau} h(\tau) d\tau$$

$$= e^{j\omega t} H(j\omega) \tag{2.29}$$

where

$$H(j\omega) = \int_{-\infty}^{\infty} e^{-j\omega \tau} h(\tau) d\tau \tag{2.30}$$

is the *Fourier transform* of the impulse response. Note that we took advantage of the commutative property of convolution to establish this result.

Example 2.3.2. Calculate the Fourier transform of the impulse response from Example 2.3.1.

Solution We simply apply Equation (2.30):

$$H(j\omega) = \int_{-\infty}^{\infty} e^{-j\omega \tau} h(\tau) d\tau$$

$$= \int_{0}^{\infty} e^{-j\omega \tau} \omega_0 e^{-\omega_0 \tau} d\tau$$

$$= \omega_0 \int_{0}^{\infty} e^{-(j\omega + \omega_0)\tau} d\tau$$

$$= \frac{\omega_0}{j\omega + \omega_0}$$

Thus, if the input to this LTIS is $x(t) = e^{j\omega t}$ then the output is

$$y(t) = \frac{\omega_0}{j\omega + \omega_0} e^{j\omega t}$$

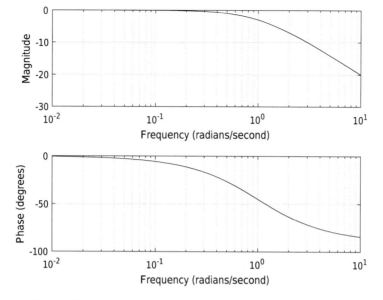

Figure 2.10: Frequency response plot for Example 2.3.3.

The Fourier transform of the impulse response, which is often called a *transfer function*, is a complex quantity that can be expressed as a real magnitude $A(\omega)$ and phase $\phi(\omega)$.

$$H(j\omega) = A(\omega)e^{j\phi(\omega)} \tag{2.31}$$

Substituting this into Equation (2.29) we have

$$y(t) = A(\omega)e^{j[\omega t + \phi(\omega)]} \tag{2.32}$$

Thus, the output of an LTIS with a sinusoidal input is a sinusoid with the same frequency, but generally a different magnitude and phase, which are frequency dependent. We refer to a plot of the magnitude and/or phase of $H(j\omega)$ as a *frequency response plot*.

Example 2.3.3. Determine the magnitude and phase of the transfer function from Example 2.3.2

Solution The result of straightforward calculation is

$$A(\omega) = \frac{\omega_0}{\sqrt{\omega_0^2 + \omega^2}}$$
$$\phi(\omega) = \tan^{-1}\omega/\omega_0$$

Figure 2.10 shows a frequency response plot for this transfer function with $\omega_0 = 1$.

It turns out that the transfer function is useful for more than just sinusoidal inputs. If we return to the general case and compute the Fourier transform of the

Function	Fourier Transform
$e^{-\omega_0 t} u(t)$	$\dfrac{1}{\omega_0 + j\omega}$
$e^{j\omega_0 t}$	$2\pi\delta(\omega - \omega_0)$
$\cos(\omega_0 t)$	$\pi[\delta(\omega + \omega_0) + \delta(\omega - \omega_0)]$
$\sin(\omega_0 t)$	$j\pi[\delta(\omega + \omega_0) - \delta(\omega - \omega_0)]$
$\delta(t)$	1
$u(t)$	$\pi\delta(\omega) + \dfrac{1}{j\omega}$

Table 2.2: Some Fourier transform pairs.

output, we have

$$
\begin{aligned}
Y(j\omega) &= \int_{-\infty}^{\infty} e^{-j\omega t} y(t)dt \\
&= \int_{-\infty}^{\infty} e^{-j\omega t} \int_{-\infty}^{\infty} h(t - \tau)x(\tau)d\tau dt \\
&= \int_{-\infty}^{\infty} \int_{-\infty}^{\infty} e^{-j\omega(t-\tau)} h(t - \tau) e^{-j\omega\tau} x(\tau) d\tau dt \\
&= \int_{-\infty}^{\infty} e^{-j\omega(t-\tau)} h(t - \tau)dt \int_{-\infty}^{\infty} e^{-j\omega\tau} x(\tau)d\tau \\
&= H(j\omega)X(j\omega) \qquad\qquad (2.33)
\end{aligned}
$$

This remarkable result is known as the *convolution theorem* and states that if $X(j\omega)$, $Y(j\omega)$, and $H(j\omega)$ are the Fourier transforms of $x(t)$, $y(t)$, and $h(t)$, respectively, and $y(t) = h(t) * x(t)$, then $Y(j\omega) = H(j\omega)X(j\omega)$. Thus, we can find the Fourier transform of the output of an LTIS by simply multiplying the Fourier transforms of the impulse response and the input signal. Moreover, we can apply the inverse Fourier transform to determine the output itself. The inverse Fourier transform is given by

$$
y(t) = \frac{1}{2\pi} \int_{-\infty}^{\infty} e^{j\omega t} Y(j\omega)d\omega \qquad\qquad (2.34)
$$

A signal and its Fourier transform are often referred to as a Fourier transform pair, and their relationship is often noted as, for example,

$$
x(t) \Leftrightarrow X(j\omega)
$$

Table 2.2 lists a few useful Fourier transform pairs. More comprehensive lists can be found in [6] and on the Internet.

Example 2.3.4. Use the convolution theorem to solve Example 2.3.1.

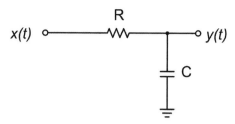

Figure 2.11: Linear circuit example.

Solution In order to avoid confusion (and error), we will denote the sinusiodal input as $x(t) = e^{j\omega_s t}$. From Table 2.2 we find that

$$e^{j\omega_s t} \Leftrightarrow 2\pi\delta(\omega - \omega_s)$$

Thus, $Y(j\omega)$ is given by

$$Y(j\omega) = \frac{\omega_0}{j\omega + \omega_0} 2\pi\delta(\omega - \omega_s)$$

The inverse transform of $Y(j\omega)$ is

$$y(t) = \frac{1}{2\pi} \int_{-\infty}^{\infty} \frac{\omega_0}{j\omega + \omega_0} 2\pi\delta(\omega - \omega_s) e^{j\omega t} d\omega$$
$$= \frac{\omega_0 e^{j\omega_s t}}{j\omega_s + \omega_0}$$

which, except for the change of notation, is identical to the result of Example 2.3.1.

The Fourier transform of a signal converts the signal from a function of time t to a function of frequency ω (or $f = 2\pi/\omega$). The Fourier transform of a signal is sometimes called the *frequency domain* representation of the signal and a plot of the magnitude of the Fourier transform is sometimes called the *spectrum* of the signal. The fact that the Fourier transform allows negative frequencies should cause no alarm – they are just a mathematical artifact. For an audio signal, the magnitude of the Fourier transform is insignificant for frequencies above the audio range (i.e., $|f| > 20$ kHz).

2.3.2 Differential Equation Model of an LTIS

Consider the simple circuit shown in Figure 2.11. The input voltage is $x(t)$ and the output voltage is $y(t)$. Applying Kirchoff's current law, we have

$$C\frac{dy(t)}{dt} + [y(t) - x(t)]/R = 0$$

from which we obtain the following relation between $x(t)$ and $y(t)$:

$$\frac{dy(t)}{dt} + \omega_0 y(t) = \omega_0 x(t)$$

where $\omega_0 = 1/RC$. This circuit is clearly linear, and none of the components is time varying, so the circuit is an LTIS. This property is also evident from the fact that the circuit is described by a linear differential equation with constant coefficients. If we assume that $x(t) = 0$ for $t < 0$ and $y(0) = 0$, then the solution to this equation is given by

$$y(t) = \omega_0 \int_0^t e^{\omega_0(t-\tau)} x(\tau) d\tau$$

Note that the circuit is an LTIS with the same impulse response as in the examples in Section 2.3.1.

A more general differential equation model of an LTIS is given by

$$\frac{d^n y(t)}{dt^n} + a_{n-1}\frac{d^{n-1}y(t)}{dt^{n-1}} + \cdots + a_1\frac{dy(t)}{dt} + a_0 y(t) =$$
$$b_n\frac{d^n x(t)}{dt^n} + b_{n-1}\frac{d^{n-1}x(t)}{dt^{n-1}} + \cdots + b_1\frac{dx(t)}{dt} + b_0 x(t) \quad (2.35)$$

There are many ways to deal with Equation (2.35), and a thorough discussion of these methods is beyond the scope of this book. Our goal here, rather, is to show the relation between Equation (2.35) and the impulse response model.

The Laplace transform method is a well-known way to solve linear ordinary differential equations with constant coefficients, and Equation (2.35) is just such an equation. The *unilateral* Laplace transform of a signal $x(t)$ is defined as

$$X(s) = \int_0^\infty e^{-st} x(t) dt$$
$$= \mathcal{L}\{x(t)\} \quad (2.36)$$

where s is a complex number often written as

$$s = \sigma + j\omega \quad (2.37)$$

where σ is the real part and ω is the imaginary part. Table 2.3 is a list of a few Laplace transform pairs, and Table 2.4 lists a few useful properties of the Laplace transform. The notation 0^- refers to a time that is just less than zero. Detailed information about Laplace transforms can be found in many references, such as [6].

The following is a more general property of the Laplace transform of a time derivative:

$$\mathcal{L}\{\frac{d^n x(t)}{dt^n}\} = s^n X(s) - s^{(n-1)} x(0^-) - \cdots - x^{(n-1)}(0^-) \quad (2.38)$$

where

$$x^{(k)}(0^-) = \frac{d^k x(t)}{dt^k}\bigg|_{t=0^-} \quad (2.39)$$

For simplicity, we will assume that all of these initial values are 0 for both $x(t)$ and $y(t)$. Then the Laplace transform of Equation (2.35) is

$$(s^n + a_{n-1}s^{n-1} + \cdots + a_1 s + a_0)Y(s) =$$
$$(b_n s^n + b_{n-1}s^{n-1} + \cdots + b_1 s + b_0)X(s) \quad (2.40)$$

Function	Laplace Transform
$\delta(t)$	1
$u(t)$	$\dfrac{1}{s}$
$e^{at}u(t)$	$\dfrac{1}{s-a}$
$\cos(\omega_0 t)u(t)$	$\dfrac{s}{s^2+\omega_0^2}$
$\sin(\omega_0 t)u(t)$	$\dfrac{\omega_0^2}{s^2+\omega_0^2}$

Table 2.3: Some Laplace transform pairs.

Function	Laplace Transform
$x_1(t)+x_2(t)$	$X_1(s)+X_2(s)$
$\dfrac{dx(t)}{dt}$	$sX(s)-x(0^-)$
$\int_{0^-}^{t} x(\tau)d\tau$	$\dfrac{1}{s}X(s)$
$x(t-t_0)u(t-t_0)$	$X(s)e^{-st_0}$
$x_1(t)*x_2(t)$	$X_1(s)X_2(s)$

Table 2.4: Some Laplace transform properties.

so that

$$Y(s) = \frac{b_n s^n + b_{n-1} s^{n-1} + \cdots + b_1 s + b_0}{s^n + a_{n-1} s^{n-1} + \cdots + a_1 s + a_0} X(s)$$
$$= H(s)X(s) \tag{2.41}$$

The function $H(s)$ is a transfer function similar to $H(j\omega)$ in Equation (2.33). Moreover, since the Laplace transform of an impulse function $\delta(t)$ is 1, the Laplace transform of the impulse response is $Y(s) = H(s)$ and therefore $H(s)$ is the Laplace transform of the impulse response $h(t)$. This can also be shown as follows:

$$Y(s) = \int_0^\infty e^{-st} \int_{-\infty}^\infty h(t-\tau)x(\tau)d\tau dt$$
$$= \int_0^\infty \left[\int_\tau^\infty e^{-st} h(t-\tau)dt \right] x(\tau)d\tau$$
$$= \int_0^\infty H(s)e^{-s\tau} x(\tau)d\tau = H(s)X(s) \tag{2.42}$$

The lower limit of the inner integral in the second line of Equation (2.42) is τ, because $h(t) = 0$ for $t < 0$. Equation (2.42) confirms the convolution property of the Laplace transform as listed in Table 2.4.

Now consider the response $y(t)$ when the input is $x(t) = e^{j\omega t}$, assuming that the system is in steady state, i.e., all responses to initial conditions have died out. Note that this is *not* the same as the response to $x(t) = e^{j\omega t}u(t)$. In this case we can assume that $y(t) = A(\omega)e^{j[\omega t + \phi(\omega)]}$. All of the derivative terms have the following simple form:

$$\frac{d^n x(t)}{dt^n} = (j\omega)^n e^{j\omega t} \tag{2.43}$$

$$\frac{d^n y(t)}{dt^n} = (j\omega)^n A(\omega)e^{j[\omega t + \phi(\omega)]} \tag{2.44}$$

Substituting this into Equation (2.35), we have

$$[(j\omega)^n + a_{n-1}(j\omega)^{n-1} + \cdots + a_1(j\omega) + a_0] A(\omega)e^{j[\omega t + \phi(\omega)]}$$
$$= [b_n(j\omega)^n + b_{n-1}(j\omega)^{n-1} + \cdots + b_1(j\omega) + b_0]e^{j\omega t} \tag{2.45}$$

The magnitude $A(\omega)$ and phase $\phi(\omega)$ of the response are therefore given by

$$A(\omega)e^{j\phi(\omega)} = \frac{b_n(j\omega)^n + b_{n-1}(j\omega)^{n-1} + \cdots + b_1(j\omega) + b_0}{(j\omega)^n + a_{n-1}(j\omega)^{n-1} + \cdots + a_1(j\omega) + a_0}$$
$$= H(j\omega) \tag{2.46}$$

Thus, we can determine the frequency response of the LTIS from the transfer function $H(s)$ by substituting $s = j\omega$.

Example 2.3.5. Figure 2.12 is a circuit model for a magnetic guitar pickup [26]. Determine the transfer function $H(s) = V_o(s)/V_s(s)$ and plot the frequency response for $L = 2$ H, $R = 5$ kΩ and $C = 100$ pF.

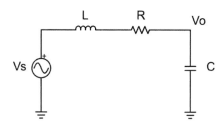

Figure 2.12: Circuit model of guitar pickup.

Solution Applying Kirchoff's voltage law, we have

$$-v_s + L\frac{di}{dt} + Ri + v_o = 0$$

We also have

$$i = C\frac{dv_o}{dt}$$

Combining these two, we have

$$-v_s + LC\frac{d^2v_o}{dt^2} + RC\frac{dv_o}{dt} + v_o = 0$$

Applying the Laplace transform gives us

$$-V_s + s^2LCV_o + sRCV_o + V_o = 0$$

so that

$$\frac{V_o(s)}{V_s(s)} = \frac{1}{s^2LC + RCs + 1}$$

Of course we can apply the Laplace transform directly to the circuit by replacing the inductance L. the resistance R, and the capacitance C with complex impedances sL, R, and $1/sC$, respectively. This leads immediately to

$$\frac{V_o(s)}{V_s(s)} = \frac{1/sC}{sL + R + 1/sC}$$
$$= \frac{1}{s^2LC + RCs + 1}$$

We will use MATLAB [11] to ease the burden of creating the frequency response plot. The MATLAB function `freqs` computes the frequency response of an LTIS directly from the transfer function. This function is used in the following script to create the frequency response plot shown in Figure 2.13.

```
L=2; R=5e3; C=100e−12;
b=1;
a=[L*C R*C 1];
[h,w]=freqs(b,a);
```

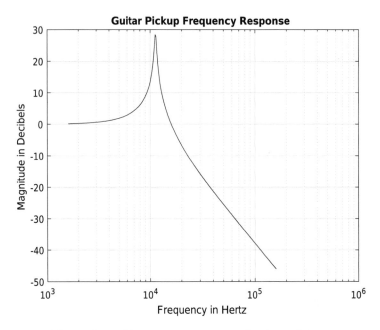

Figure 2.13: Frequency response of guitar pickup.

```
f=w/(2*pi);
semilogx(f,20*log10(abs(h)));
grid on
title('Guitar␣Pickup␣Frequency␣Response')
xlabel('Frequency␣in␣Hz')
ylabel('Magnitude␣in␣dB')
```

A MATLAB script is simply a sequence of executable MATLAB programming statements. The first statement, which is actually three statements on one line, assigns
values of L, R, and C to appropriately named MATLAB variables. The next two
statements assign the transfer function coefficient values to the numerator array **b**
and the denominator array **a**. The next line is the call to `freqs`, which, when called
in this manner, computes the complex frequency response at 200 uniformly spaced
frequencies. The frequency responses and corresponding frequencies are returned in
arrays **h** and **w**, respectively. The remainder of the script converts the frequencies
from radians/second to hertz and plots the magnitude of the frequency response (in
decibels) using a logarithmic scale for the frequency axis.

2.4   Summary

In this chapter we have examined a few basic analog audio signals and introduced
the notion of processing these signals with an analog linear time-invariant system
(LTIS). We have seen that the sinusoidal signal, which by itself produces a pure audio tone, is the building block for a much larger class of signals. We have, therefore,
invested some effort to see how an LTIS responds to sinusoidal input and determined

how to calculate the frequency response of an LTIS. We have also introduced the Fourier and Laplace transforms, two very important and useful signal-processing tools, and examined some of their properties, most notably their convolution properties.

In Chapter 3 we will make the transition from the continuous-time analog domain to the discrete-time digital domain, and in Chapter 4 we will study digital signals and digital LTIS. We will find that the signals, systems, and tools from the analog world have counterparts in the digital world.

Exercises

1. (a) Convert the following RMS acoustic pressure levels to dB SPL: 50 μPa, 20 Pa, 5 μPa,

   (b) Convert the following dB SPL values to acoustic pressure in Pa: 40 dB SPL, 80 dB SPL, -10 dB SPL.

2. The total power of the square wave in Example 2.2.1 is given by A^2. Determine the percentage of the total power contained in the fundamental component of its Fourier series.

3. Show that the output of the LTIS of Example 2.3.1 when the input is a unit step function is $y(t) = 1 - e^{-\omega_0 t}$.

MATLAB Projects

These and many exercises in this book are based on the use of MATLAB. Use of MATLAB or similar software allows one to apply the concepts and methods presented in this book to complex audio signals and systems. It can even be used to develop useful tools, or at least prototype tools, for audio engineering. This book assumes little prior knowledge beyond basic programming and uses a very small subset of MATLAB capabilities.

This first set of MATLAB exercises includes step-by-step instructions to produce the MATLAB code. By completing all of the exercises, the student will build up some facility with MATLAB and require less guidance.

1. Generate and plot a few cycles of a sinusoidal signal with frequency 100 Hz and amplitude 5 V.

   (a) First note that the period of the signal is 0.01 s so that an interval of $T = 0.03$ s will include 3 cycles. In order to obtain a reasonably smooth plot we will divide this interval into $N = 100$ points in time. The MATLAB function **linspace** makes this easy:

   ```
   T=0.03;
   N=100;
   t=linspace(0,T,N);
   ```

   This sequence of MATLAB commands generates an array t of 100 points in time distributed uniformly between 0 and 0.03 s.

(b) Next we generate the sinusoidal signal using the MATLAB function **sin**.
The code is simply

```
A=5;
f=100;
x=sin(2*pi*f*t);
```

Note that the **sin** function, like many similar MATLAB functions, produces an array output for an array input. Thus, x is an array of N values
of the sinusoidal signal. The constant **pi** is predefined in MATLAB.

(c) Finally, we use the MATLAB **plot** function to produce a nice graph of
the signal.

```
plot(t,x);
title('Sinusoidal_Signal');
xlabel('Time_in_Seconds');
ylabel('Amplitude');
```

2. The object of this exercise is to play a sinusoidal signal using the MATLAB
function **sound**. The **sound** function requires two inputs: the signal values
at uniformly spaced points in time and the *sampling frequency*, which we will
take for now as the inverse of the interval between the adjacent points in time.
We will learn more about the sampling frequency in Chapter 3. The signal
values for a sinusoidal signal can be produced by repeating Exercise 1, but
with larger values for T and N. For the purposes of this exercise, let $T = 3$ s
and let $N = f_s T$, where $f_s = 44\,100$ Hz is the sampling frequency (this is one
of the standard values for f_s). Thus, the procedure of Exercise 1 will produce
$N = 132\,300$ values of the sinusoidal signal covering 300 cycles. These values
can be passed to the **sound** function to produce the sound, using the host
computer's audio hardware. In summary, the MATLAB code is

```
f=100;
fs=44100;
T=3;
N=fs*T;
t=linspace(0,T,N);
x=sin(2*pi*f*t);
sound(x,fs);
```

3. For this exercise you will need a small audio file (a few seconds of music,
speech, or other interesting audio) in one of the common formats (e.g., **.wav**).
The MATLAB function **audioread** can be used to obtain an array of values
of the signal in the audio file as well as the sampling frequency:

```
[x,fs]=audioread('<file>');
```

where <file> is the name of the audio file (including the file extension). Note
the convention for a MATLAB function that returns more than one object.
You can immediately play the signal using the **sound** function. You can also
plot the signal by simply using the command **plot(x)**. However, it is better

to include the time axis, and for this you need the array t. The number of signal values N can be determined using the MATLAB length function:

N=**length** (x) ;

Since the duration of the signal is $T = N/f_s$, the array t can be determined using linspace

t=**linspace** (0 ,N/ fs ,N) ;

Some prefer, however, to compute t as

t = (0:N−1)/ fs ;

In MATLAB the expression M:N is an array of integers ranging from M to N, inclusive (both M and N should be integers). In either case plot(t,x) will produce the desired result.

Chapter 3

Digital Coding of Sound

In the preceding chapters the audio signal was modeled as a continuous function of time $x(t)$, i.e., an analog signal. Until around the 1960s all audio equipment was designed to process (e.g., amplify, equalize, etc.) analog signals. In the mid-1960s things began to change, starting in the telecommunications industry. Bell Laboratories developed transmission systems that transmitted audio signals as a sequence of electrical pulses representing binary numbers (0s and 1s). Over the next few decades, this new digital technology took over nearly the entire worldwide telecommunications network and now nearly all information (text, audio, video, data) is processed and communicated in a digital format (i.e., electrical or optical pulses representing 0s and 1s).

The digital revolution has had a profound effect on the audio industry as well. Compact disks and digital audiotapes replaced vinyl recordings and are in turn being replaced by streaming audio and downloadable digital files. Electronic digital recorders have replaced tape recorders, and digital technology is being used enhance audio quality and create audio effects. Hardware and software are available to convert your home computer to a recording studio.

This chapter describes the most basic process of converting an analog signal to a digital format, a process known as pulse-code modulation or PCM. The reverse process, converting a digital signal back to analog, is also covered.

3.1 Digital Representation of an Analog Signal

An analog signal $x(t)$ with finite duration T is defined for all values of t in the continuous-time domain $[0, T]$, and $x(t)$ can take on any value in the continuous range $[X_{\min}, X_{\max}]$. The digital representation of this signal is a sequence of L-bit binary numbers $b(n)$ representing values of the signal at N evenly distributed discrete points in the time domain. The digital representation cannot exactly match the analog signal for these two reasons:

- Only N instants of time are chosen from the continuous-time domain, which contains an uncountable number of instants.

- An L-bit binary number can only represent 2^L values, whereas $x(t)$ can assume an uncountable number of values, even if its range is limited.

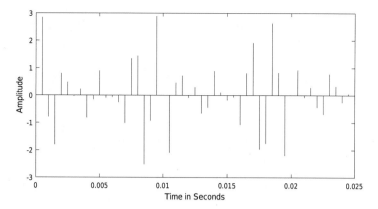

Figure 3.1: Samples of the triad signal.

Thus, converting a signal from analog to digital results in some loss of information, and this loss must be kept to a level such that the original analog signal can be recovered from the digital representation to some degree of accuracy.

PCM, which is sometimes referred to as a kind of *waveform coding*, is certainly not the only way to digitize an analog signal, but it is one of the most common methods and is a component of some of the more sophisticated methods such as differential PCM and MPEG (Motion Picture Experts Group) coding. We will describe the PCM process in terms of two sub-processes: *sampling* and *quantizing*

3.2 Sampling

Sampling is the first step in the analog-to-digital conversion process. In this step, the value of $x(t)$ is captured at a sequence of discrete points in time. This can be expressed mathematically as

$$x_s(n) = x(n\tau_s) = x(n/f_s) \tag{3.1}$$

where $x_s(n)$ is the nth sample, τ_s is the *sampling interval*, i.e., the time between successive samples, and f_s is the *sampling frequency*, i.e., the rate at which samples are taken. To simplify notation, we will omit the subscript s and let $x(n)$ represent the sampled version of the analog signal $x(t)$. The total number of samples taken during the interval $[0, T]$ is $N = f_s T$ (rounded or truncated to an integer). Figure 3.1 shows the result of sampling the major triad in Figure 2.4 at the rate of 2000 Hz (in the context of sampling, the unit hertz is often used in place of samples/second). In this example, an audio signal of 25 ms duration is represented by 51 samples (one sample every 0.5 ms). Samples are shown as vertical lines representing narrow pulses.

The sampling process is quite straightforward and can be implemented with fairly simple electronics. The reverse process, recovering the original analog signal from the samples, is also straightforward, until one asks how well the recovered signal matches the original. Recovery processes are based on some form of interpolation under the assumption that nothing too crazy happens between successive samples. The *Nyquist criterion* provides the means to establish the required sanity, at least

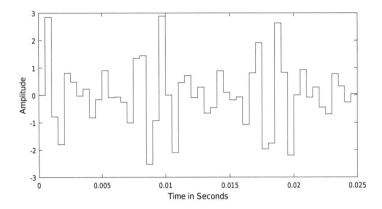

Figure 3.2: Triad signal: sample and hold.

for *band limited* signals. A band limited signal is one for which the spectrum (as given by the Fourier transform) is zero for all frequencies above some upper limit F. The Nyquist criterion states that the sampling frequency should be at least twice the upper limit, i.e.,

$$f_s \geq 2F \tag{3.2}$$

The example meets this criterion, since the highest frequency in the triad is 660 Hz and the sampling rate is 2 kHz. This means that it should be possible to recover the original signal fairly well from the samples. The sampling rate for audio compact disks (CDs) is 44.1 kHz, which is somewhat more than twice the highest frequency that humans can hear. Some musical recording systems operate at higher rates (as high as 192 kHz currently). The standard sampling rate for voice communication is 8 kHz, which proves to be adequate for speech understanding and even speaker recognition, but is not very satisfactory for music or other high-fidelity sound.

The Nyquist criterion is sometimes stated in terms of the *Nyquist frequency* F_N, given by

$$F_N = \frac{f_s}{2} \tag{3.3}$$

For a given sampling rate, the audio signal should be band limited at or below the Nyquist frequency.

How well can one recover the original analog signal from the samples? The Nyquist theory provides a formula that can exactly reproduce the original signal from the samples, provided Equation (3.2) is satisfied. However, this formula includes a summation over an infinite sequence of samples and must be approximated in practice. On the other hand, a simple "hold and filter" approach works quite well. In this approach the sequence of samples is input to a holding device with a continuous output equal to the value of the most recent sample. The output of this device for the samples in Figure 3.1 is shown in Figure 3.2. The held sample output bears some resemblance to the original signal, but is still rather crude. It is interesting to view the spectrum (i.e., Fourier transform) of the held sample output as shown in Figure 3.3.[1] The three components of the triad are still present,

---

[1]The Fourier transform for Figure 3.3 was obtained using a numerical algorithm.

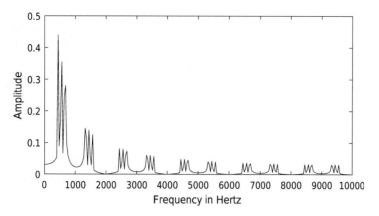

Figure 3.3: Fourier transform of triad sample and hold.

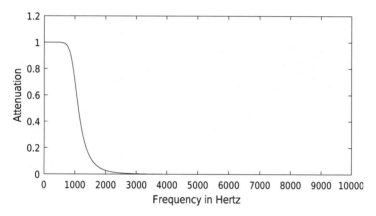

Figure 3.4: Low-pass filter frequency response.

but they have been joined by additional components, called *harmonics*, at higher frequencies. It would seem, therefore, that a better approximation of the original signal could be obtained by eliminating these harmonics. This can be done with a low-pass filter, a device that is transparent to low frequencies but suppresses higher frequencies.[2] An ideal low-pass filter, which cannot be realized in practice, would eliminate all frequency components above a cutoff frequency and have no effect on frequencies below the cutoff frequency. Practical filters introduce attenuation that varies with frequency. In a low-pass filter, there is little or no attenuation below the cutoff frequency, but as the frequency increases beyond the cutoff frequency the attenuation increases rapidly, suppressing higher-frequency components. Figure 3.4 shows the frequency response of a practical low-pass filter with a cutoff frequency of 1000 Hz. Figure 3.5 shows the output of this filter when the input is the held sample signal in Figure 3.2. The original signal is included for comparison. Note that except for some delay and attenuation, the recovered signal is a good match to the original.

---

[2]The low-pass filter is one of several frequency-shaping filters discussed in Chapter 6.

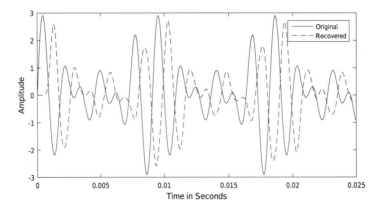

Figure 3.5: Original and recovered triad signal.

To summarize:

- The sampling process obtains a sequence of samples from an analog signal by taking the values of the signal at regularly spaced points in time.

- In order to preserve sufficient information to reconstruct the original analog signal, the sampling frequency should satisfy the Nyquist criterion as given in Equation (3.2).

- The analog signal can be recovered from the samples by interpolation and filtering. The hold-and-filter approach is an example based on zero-order interpolation.

3.2.1   Aliasing

Suppose that a signal is sampled at a rate f_s and the signal spectrum contains components at frequencies greater than the Nyquist frequency $f_s/2$. Then, according to the Nyquist theorem, it will not be possible to recover the original signal accurately, even using an infinite number of samples. One solution to this problem would be to raise the sampling rate so that all components of the signal spectrum are below the Nyquist frequency. However, this ideal cannot be achieved in practice, because no real signal is truly band limited. So it is inevitable that some components will lie above the Nyquist frequency, and the effects of these components must be understood.

The fact that components above the Nyquist frequency are lost may not be a problem. For example, in a voice communication system, frequencies above 4000 Hz do not significantly enhance intelligibility. Unfortunately, loss of high-frequency components is not the only consequence of *undersampling*. Components above the Nyquist frequency can create corresponding components below the Nyquist frequency that are not present in the original signal spectrum. These components are known as *alias* components and can create significant distortion. Figure 3.6 illustrates a 1000 Hz sine wave sampled at a rate of 1200 Hz. The frequency of the sine wave is clearly above the Nyquist frequency, which is 600 Hz. Note that a 200 Hz sine wave, which falls below the Nyquist frequency, fits the samples exactly.

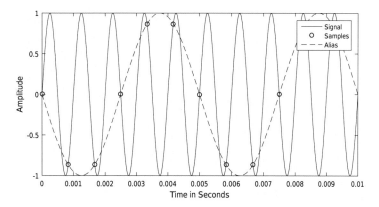

Figure 3.6: An alias signal.

Thus, a 1000 Hz sine wave sampled at 1200 Hz will be recovered as a 200 Hz sine wave – not a good result. In general, a component at frequency f_c between $f_s/2$ and f_s will produce an alias at frequency $f_a = f_s - f_c$. Fortunately, aliasing can be avoided even if it is not practical or desirable to increase the sampling frequency. The solution is to pass the original analog signal through an aliasing filter prior to sampling. The aliasing filter is a low-pass filter that is designed to eliminate components above the Nyquist frequency prior to sampling. The high-frequency components are still lost, but their annoying aliases are lost along with them.

3.2.2 Down- and Upsampling

There are a number of sampling rates in use in the audio industry and it is sometimes necessary to convert among them. For example, a digital audio workstation in a recording studio may produce audio files with sampling rates of 96 kHz or 192 kHz and these may in turn be used to create a CD with a sampling rate of 44.1 kHz. In this section we will present some basic methods for *resampling*, i.e., changing the sampling rate.

The simplest kind of resampling is to decrease or increase the sampling rate by an integer factor. The downsampling operation is defined simply as

$$x_D(n) = x(nL) \tag{3.4}$$

where $x(n)$ is the input signal, $x_D(n)$ is the downsampled output, and L is the downsampling factor. This operation is denoted $\downarrow L$. The upsampling operation, denoted $\uparrow L$, is defined as

$$x_U(n) = \begin{cases} x(n/L) & n \bmod L = 0 \\ 0 & n \bmod L \neq 0 \end{cases} \tag{3.5}$$

Figure 3.7 illustrates both down- and upsampling of a sinusoid. The MATLAB functions `downsample` and `upsample` were used to generate this figure.

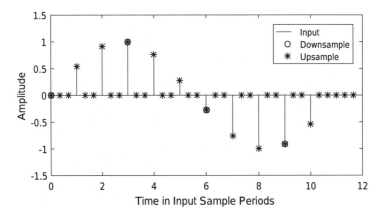

Figure 3.7: Down- and upsampling of a signal ($L = 3$).

3.2.3   Resampling Methods

The basic down- and upsampling described in Section 3.2.2 are clearly quite limited, but can play a role in more sophisticated methods. In this section we will address the general problem of changing the sampling rate of an audio signal from one frequency (f_1) to another (f_2). We will consider two approaches:

- Derive a continuous time version of the input signal using interpolation and sample the derived signal at the new rate.

- Upsample the input signal by an integer factor p, low-pass filter the result, and downsample the filter output by an integer factor q. The ratio p/q should closely match the ratio f_2/f_1.

Resampling by Linear Interpolation

The simplest example of the interpolation approach is based on linear interpolation. The input signal $x(n)$ has length N (i.e., $n = 0, 1, \ldots, N - 1$) and sampling rate f_x, and we wish resample $x(n)$ to create signal $y(m)$ with sampling rate f_y. Since the duration of $x(n)$ is $(N - 1)/f_x$, the length of $y(m)$ should be the largest integer M such that

$$\frac{M - 1}{f_y} \leq \frac{N - 1}{f_x} \tag{3.6}$$

This leads to a length of

$$M = \lfloor (N - 1)f_y/f_x \rfloor + 1 \tag{3.7}$$

where the L-brackets denote the floor function, i.e., the most positive integer that is less than or equal to the enclosed quantity. The sampling times for $y(m)$ are $t_m = m/f_y$, but it is convenient to express these times in terms of the sampling period of the input signal.

$$u_m = t_m/\tau_x$$
$$= \frac{m f_x}{f_y} \tag{3.8}$$

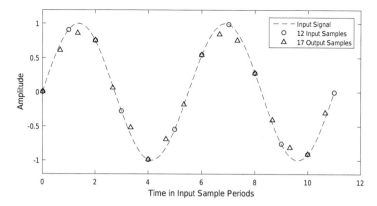

Figure 3.8: Resampling using linear interpolation ($f_x = 32\,000$, $f_y = 48\,000$).

Output sample $y(m)$ lies between input samples $x(n_m)$ and $x(n_m + 1)$ where

$$n_m = \lfloor u_m \rfloor \tag{3.9}$$

and the interpolated value $y(m)$ is given by

$$y(m) = x(n_m)(1 - \Delta u_m) + x(n_m + 1)\Delta u_m \tag{3.10}$$

where $\Delta u_m = u_m - n_m$. Figure 3.8 shows an example of this resampling method.

Resampling by Up- and Downsampling

If we upsample a signal $x(n)$ by an integer factor p and downsample the result by an integer factor q, then we change the sampling rate by factor p/q. Unfortunately this straightforward approach does not work, because the intermediate result is mostly zeros. This problem can be solved, however, by inserting a low-pass filter between the upsampling and downsampling steps. The MATLAB function **resample** [11] implements a version of this procedure when invoked as

y=resample(x,p,q);

In this case the function designs a suitable low-pass filter, and calls MATLAB function **upfirdn** to carry out the up-filter-down process. The **resample** function adjusts the filter and its output to obtain the appropriate amplitude and timing of the output. Figure 3.9 illustrates an example application of **resample**.

3.3 Quantizing

In the quantizing step, each sample $x(n)$ is converted to an integer $Q(n)$ that can be coded as an L-bit binary number. This can be expressed mathematically as

$$Q(n) = f[x(n)] \tag{3.11}$$

where $f(x)$ is a suitable quantizing function. The quantized value $Q(n)$ is normally an integer in the range $-2^{L-1} \le Q(n) < 2^{L-1}$, although the endpoints of the range

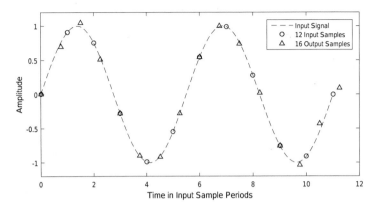

Figure 3.9: Resampling using MATLAB `resample` function ($p = 4$, $q = 3$).

may vary with the quantizing algorithm. Positive values of $Q(n)$ are represented by their binary equivalents, and negative values are represented with the two's complement of the corresponding positive value.[3] Equation (3.11) is a many-to-one mapping, in that a given value of $Q(n)$ corresponds to a range of values of $x(n)$.

Linear quantizing is the most straightforward quantizing method and is used widely. Linear quantizing can be expressed as (dropping the sample index n)

$$Q = \lfloor Ax + B \rfloor \tag{3.12}$$

Assume that the range of x is $-1 \le x \le 1$. Ignoring the floor function for the moment, the corresponding range of Q is from $Q_{min} = -A + B$ to $Q_{max} = A + B$. Thus, we might calculate A and B as

$$A = \frac{Q_{max} - Q_{min}}{2}$$
$$B = \frac{Q_{max} + Q_{min}}{2} \tag{3.13}$$

For example, suppose we choose $Q_{max} = 2^{L-1}$ and $Q_{min} = -2^{L-1}$. Then it follows from Equation (3.13) that $A = 2^{L-1}$ and $B = 0$. Figure 3.10 is a plot of Equation (3.12) for $L = 4$ that shows the quantized value increasing in steps from -8 to $+7$ (assuming appropriate handling of the case where $x = 1$). Figure 3.11 shows how the quantization changes if we choose $Q_{max} = 2^{L-1}$ and $Q_{min} = -2^{L-1} + 1$. The quantized value now ranges from -7 to $+7$, a loss of one step. On the other hand, there is no longer a step at $x = 0$, which can overemphasize a weak signal that is hovering in the neighborhood of $x = 0$. We will refer to the latter version as *symmetrical linear quantizing*.

Example 3.3.1. Encode the sample values $x = 0.72$ and $x = -0.34$ using symmetrical linear quantization with $L = 5$ bits.

---

[3]The two's complement of a binary number is obtained by inverting each digit (change 0 to 1 and 1 to 0) and adding 1 to the result, ignoring overflow.

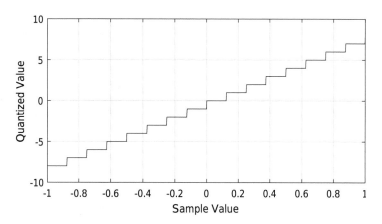

Figure 3.10: Linear quantization function: $Q_{\max} = 2^{L-1}$ and $Q_{\min} = -2^{L-1}$.

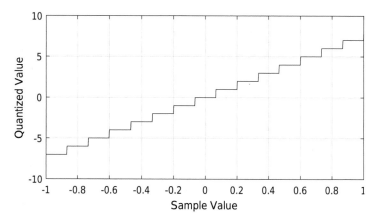

Figure 3.11: Linear quantization function: $Q_{\max} = 2^{L-1}$ and $Q_{\min} = -2^{L-1} + 1$.

Solution The quantization function coefficients are $A = 2^{5-1} - 0.5 = 15.5$ and $B = 0.5$. For $x = 0.72$ the quantized value is

$$Q = \lfloor 15.5 \times 0.72 + 0.5 \rfloor$$
$$= \lfloor 11.66 \rfloor = 11$$

The corresponding binary code is 01011. For $x = -0.34$ we have

$$Q = \lfloor 15.5 \times (-0.34) + 0.5 \rfloor$$
$$= \lfloor -4.77 \rfloor = -5$$

The 5-bit binary code for 5 is 00101 and the two's complement of this number is $11010 + 00001 = 11011$.

Example 3.3.2. Write a MATLAB function to solve Example 3.3.1.

Solution The following function determines the N-bit binary code for sample value x:

```
function bits=encode(x,N)
if x >= 1
    x=1-eps;
elseif x < -1
    x=-1;
end
A=2^(N-1)-0.5;
B=0.5;
Q=floor(A*x+B);
if Q < 0
    Q=Q+2^N;
end
bits=dec2bin(Q,N);
```

Initially, the sample value x is adjusted to make sure that values outside the range $-1 \le x < 1$ are coded correctly. Calculation of A, B, and Q is straightforward. Since the MATLAB function **dec2bin** is limited to nonnegative values of Q, such values are shifted by 2^N to achieve the two's complement coding.

Since the encoding process is a many-to-one mapping that maps a range of sample values into one code, the decoding process cannot be exact. The standard solution to this dilemma is to map the binary code to the mid-point of the corresponding range. From Equation (3.12) we can see that for a given quantized value Q

$$Q \le Ax + B < Q + 1 \qquad (3.14)$$

The value of x corresponding to the middle of the range associated with Q satisfies

$$A\hat{x} + B = Q + 0.5 \qquad (3.15)$$

so that

$$\hat{x} = \frac{Q + 0.5 - B}{A} \qquad (3.16)$$

Example 3.3.3. Decode the binary codes 01011 and 11011 assuming that these codes were generated using symmetrical linear quantization with $L = 5$ bits.

Solution We previously determined that $A = 15.5$ and $B = 0.5$, so that Equation (3.16) simplifies to

$$\hat{x} = Q/A$$

The decimal equivalents of 01011 and 11011 are 11 and -5, respectively. The corresponding estimates of x are $\hat{x} = 0.7097$ and $\hat{x} = -0.3226$.

Example 3.3.4. Write a MATLAB function to solve Example 3.3.3.

Solution The following function determines the estimated sample value $\hat{x}$ corresponding to a N-bit binary code generated by the function in Example 3.3.2:

```
function x=decode(bits)
N=length(bits);
A=2^(N-1)-0.5;
Q=bin2dec(bits);
if bits(1) == '1'
    Q=Q-2^N;
end
x=Q/A;
```

The MATLAB function `bin2dec` converts the bit string to a positive decimal value. If the highest-order bit is a 1, then Q is negated by subtracting 2^N.

Table 3.1 provides another illustration of symmetrical linear quantizing. To understand this table, which is based on 4 bits/sample, consider a sample with a value of 0.5. This value falls in the range 0.4667 to 0.6000 and is thus encoded as 0100. The binary code 0100 decodes to a value of 0.5333 (the midpoint of the range). The difference between the decoded value and the actual value (0.0333) is called the *quantization error*.

Figure 3.12 summarizes the effects of both sampling and quantizing on an analog signal. It shows the original analog major triad signal, the analog signal recovered from samples of the signal ("Recovered 1"), and the analog signal recovered from the coded/decoded samples with $L = 4$ ("Recovered 2"). The Recovered 1 signal shows the effect of sampling error (along with some attenuation and delay that is not very significant). The Recovered 2 signal adds the effect of quantization error, which appears to be small, but is actually relatively large because of the small value of L in the example. The following section considers quantization error in more detail.

3.3.1 Quantization Error

Figure 3.13 is a plot of the estimated sample value and the quantization error for symmetrical linear quantizing with $L = 4$. The quantizing function divides the range of sample values ($-1 \leq x \leq 1$) into $2^L - 1 = 15$ equal intervals of length $\Delta = 1/A$. Since the quantized sample is the midpoint of the range, the quantization error can range from $-\Delta/2$ to $\Delta/2$. The amount of error for a given sample can be modeled as a random value within this range. Although random values are rather

Range			Code	
From	To	Mid	Decimal	Binary
−1.0000	−0.8667	−0.9333	−7	1001
−0.8667	−0.7333	−0.8000	−6	1010
−0.7333	−0.6000	−0.6667	−5	1011
−0.6000	−0.4667	−0.5333	−4	1100
−0.4667	−0.3333	−0.4000	−3	1101
−0.3333	−0.2000	−0.2667	−2	1110
−0.2000	−0.0667	−0.1333	−1	1111
−0.0667	0.0667	−0.0000	0	0000
0.0667	0.2000	0.1333	1	0001
0.2000	0.3333	0.2667	2	0010
0.3333	0.4667	0.4000	3	0011
0.4667	0.6000	0.5333	4	0100
0.6000	0.7333	0.6667	5	0101
0.7333	0.8667	0.8000	6	0110
0.8667	1.0000	0.9333	7	0111

Table 3.1: Coding and decoding for $L = 4$.

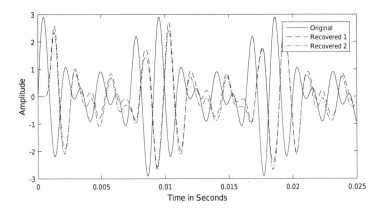

Figure 3.12: Original and recovered triad signals.

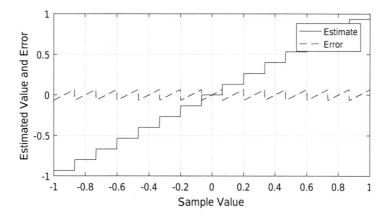

Figure 3.13: Estimated sample value and error for symmetrical linear quantizing with $L = 4$.

elusive, we can quantify their properties such as the *mean* (average of the value) or the *variance* (average of the square of the value less the mean). It can be shown that if all values in the range are equally likely, then the variance or mean squared error is given by

$$\sigma^2 = \frac{\Delta^2}{12} \tag{3.17}$$

We can express the variance in dB as

$$\begin{aligned}
\text{QN} &= 10 \log_{10} \sigma^2 \\
&= 10 \log_{10} \frac{\Delta^2}{12} \\
&= 20 \log_{10} \Delta - 10 \log_{10} 12 \\
&= -20 \log_{10} A - 10.79 \tag{3.18}
\end{aligned}$$

For large enough values of L, $A \approx 2^{L-1}$, and Equation (3.18) becomes

$$\begin{aligned}
\text{QN} &\approx -20(L-1) \log_{10} 2 - 10.79 \\
&= -6.02(L-1) - 10.79 \tag{3.19}
\end{aligned}$$

Equation (3.19), which is fairly accurate for $L \geq 4$, indicates that each additional quantizing bit reduces the quantizing error by about 6 dB.

Audio for CDs is quantized using linear quantizing with $L = 16$. This quantizing, together with the 44.1 kHz sampling rate, produces what is commonly called "CD quality sound." Music recording equipment supports higher bit depth (e.g., 24 bits).

3.3.2 Nonlinear Quantization

Linear quantizing does not necessarily provide the best quality for a given number of bits/sample. Thus, some quantizing methods use a nonlinear quantizing function in Equation (3.11). In this section we will construct a nonlinear quantizing algorithm based on the following quantizing function:

$$Q = \lfloor A \operatorname{sgn}(x) |x|^a \rfloor \tag{3.20}$$

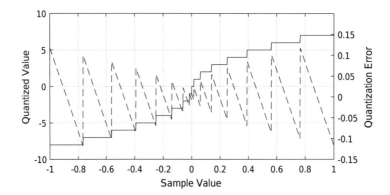

Figure 3.14: Nonlinear quantizing function $L = 4$ and $A = 0.5$.

where $A = 2^{L-1}$, $0 < a < 1$. The function sgn is known as the sign function and is defined as

$$\text{sgn}(x) = \begin{cases} -1 & x < 0 \\ 0 & x = 0 \\ 1 & x > 0 \end{cases} \tag{3.21}$$

For $-1 \le x < 1$, Q ranges from -2^{L-1} to $2^{L-1} - 1$. The solid line in Figure 3.14 is a plot of Equation (3.20) for $L = 4$ and $a = 0.5$. The figure shows that the quantization steps are smaller for values of x near 0. For a given value of Q, $x_1 \le x \le x_2$, where

$$x_1 = \text{sgn}(Q)|Q/A|^{1/a}$$
$$x_2 = \text{sgn}(Q+1)|(Q+1)/A|^{1/a} \tag{3.22}$$

Following our linear quantizing convention, we can estimate x as $\hat{x} = (x_1 + x_2)/2$. The dashed line in Figure 3.14 is a plot of the resulting estimation error. This may result in improved overall quality if the sample values are more likely to be small with relatively few excursions toward the upper or lower limits.

3.4 Summary

Figure 3.15 summarizes the entire process presented in this chapter. The starting point is an analog signal with an amplitude that varies continuously with time over a continuous range of values, and the endpoint is an acceptably accurate reconstruction of the signal. The signal is to be stored for later use or transmitted to some distant location (or both), and a digital medium offers the advantages of modern technology. The original signal $x(t)$ is filtered and sampled at a rate f_s Hz to produce a sequence of samples $x(n)$. The samples are encoded to produce a sequence $b(n)$ of L-bit binary codes using, for example, linear quantization. The binary sequence can be stored in a memory device or on a CD or transmitted electronically or optically. At some different time or place, the binary sequence is decoded to produce a sequence of estimates of the samples. The accuracy of these estimates

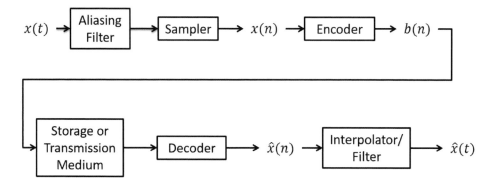

Figure 3.15: Digital audio system.

depends on the bit depth L. Finally, the interpolator/filter produces a continuous output signal that is an estimate of the original analog signal.

This chapter is limited to a mathematical and numerical description of analog-to-digital (A/D) and digital-to-analog conversion (D/A). There are a number of ways to implement these conversions (see, e.g., Chapter 10 of [27]) and devices to perform both A/D and D/A conversion are widely available. Our purpose here is to define the process and understand some of its properties and limitations.

Exercises

1. A certain digital stereo audio recording has a playing time of 2 minutes, 45 seconds. The sampling rate is 44.1 kHz (44 100 samples/s) and the bit depth is 16 bits. Determine the total number of bytes of audio data in the recording.

2. A pure sine wave with a frequency of 5000 Hz is sampled at the rate of 7000 Hz. Determine the frequency of the resulting alias signal.

3. For a symmetrical linear quantizer with $L = 8$:

   (a) Determine the binary codes for signal amplitudes of $+0.6$ and -0.8.

   (b) Determine the signal amplitude for binary codes 00001001 and 11001000.

MATLAB Exercises

1. Write a MATLAB function using the **encode** and **decode** functions presented in this chapter with input arguments x and L and outputs **xest** and **err**, where

   x = input signal vector (range $-1 \leq x(n) < 1$)

   L = bits/sample

   xest = signal recovered from coded input samples

   err = sample-by-sample difference between x and **xest**

2. Write MATLAB function `linresample` with input arguments `x`, `fx`, `fy`, and output `y`, where

   `x` = input signal vector

   `fx` = sampling rate of `x`

   `y` = output signal vector (resampled version of `x`)

   `fy` = sampling rate of `y`

   The function should use the linear interpolation method. Use this function to create a plot similar to Figure 3.8.

Chapter 4

Digital Audio Signal Processing

This chapter is about digital signals and digital LTIS. For the purposes of this chapter we will use the phrase "digital signal" to mean a sequence of real values such as you would obtain by sampling an analog signal. It might be more accurate to use the phrase "discrete-time signal," since the range of values is continuous.

The organization of this chapter is similar to that of Chapter 2. We will introduce some basic digital signals and then define a digital LTIS. We will examine two basic models of a digital LTIS and show how they are related. This chapter provides some of the basic tools needed for audio signal processing.

4.1 Basic Digital Signals

We normally assume that a digital signal $x_d(n)$ is a sampled version of an analog signal $x_a(t)$, i.e.,

$$x_d(n) = x_a(n\tau_s) \tag{4.1}$$

where $\tau_s = 1/f_s$ is the sampling interval (f_s is the sampling frequency in Hz). It is useful, however, to introduce some basic signals that are defined directly in the discrete time domain (and drop the d and a subscripts).

4.1.1 Digital Impulse Function

The digital impulse function $\delta(n)$ is defined as

$$\delta(n) = \begin{cases} 1 & n = 0 \\ 0 & n \neq 0 \end{cases} \tag{4.2}$$

Although this signal is somewhat artificial, we will make much use of it as we proceed.

4.1.2   Digital Unit Step Function

The digital unit step function $u(n)$ is defined as

$$u(n) = \begin{cases} 1 & n \geq 0 \\ 0 & n < 0 \end{cases} \tag{4.3}$$

The unit step function is often used to define a signal that starts at $n = 0$. For example, a decaying exponential pulse that starts at $n = 0$ can be expressed as

$$x(n) = \alpha^{-n} u(n) \tag{4.4}$$

where $0 < \alpha < 1$.

4.1.3   Digital Everlasting Exponential Signal

The digital everlasting exponential signal is defined as

$$x(n) = z^n \quad \forall n \tag{4.5}$$

where z is in general a complex number. In practice "everlasting" means that the signal will be present for all future time of interest and that there are no remaining artifacts of the onset of the signal.

If $z = e^{j\Omega}$, then the signal becomes a digital sinusoid, i.e.,

$$\begin{aligned} x(n) &= e^{j\Omega n} \\ &= \cos \Omega n + j \sin \Omega n \end{aligned} \tag{4.6}$$

where Ω is the frequency in *radians per sample*. Since $e^{j(\Omega + 2\pi)n} = e^{j\Omega n}$, values of $x(n)$ for Ω outside the range $0 \leq \Omega \leq 2\pi$ can be determined from values for Ω within this range. Thus, we need only be concerned about frequencies within this range.

The digital everlasting exponential signal can also be defined as a sampled version of an analog everlasting exponential signal $x(t) = e^{st}$. The sampled version is given by

$$\begin{aligned} x(n) &= e^{sn/f_s} \\ &= (e^{s/f_s})^n \end{aligned} \tag{4.7}$$

so that $z = e^{s/f_s}$. If the analog signal is sinusoidal ($x(t) = e^{j\omega t}$), then the digital version becomes

$$x(n) = e^{j\omega n / fs} \tag{4.8}$$

so that $\Omega = \omega/f_s = 2\pi f/f_s$, where f is the frequency of the analog signal in hertz. In light of previous discussion, we can limit our attention to frequencies in the range $0 \leq f \leq f_s$.

4.1.4 Periodic Digital Functions

A digital signal $x(n)$ is periodic if for some positive integer N_0

$$x(n) = x(n + N_0) \tag{4.9}$$

for all n. The period of the signal is the smallest value of N_0 that satisfies Equation (4.9).

Although the analog sinusoid is periodic regardless of its frequency ω, the same is not true for its digital counterpart. If we apply Equation (4.9) to a digital sinusoid, we have

$$e^{j\Omega n} = e^{j(\Omega n + \Omega N_0)} \tag{4.10}$$

This can only be true if ΩN_0 is an integer multiple of 2π. The smallest value of Ω for which this is true is $\Omega = \Omega_0 = 2\pi/N_0$, which is the fundamental frequency of a digital sinusoid with period N_0.

4.2 Digital LTIS

A digital LTIS is just that: an LTIS with a digital input $x(n)$ and a digital output $y(n)$. The basic properties of a digital LTIS are:

- Linearity – If input $x_1(n)$ produces output $y_1(n)$ and input $x_2(n)$ produces output $y_2(n)$, then input $ax_1(n) + bx_2(n)$ produces output $ay_1(n) + by_2(n)$.

- Time-invariance – If input $x(n)$ produces output $y(n)$, then input $x(n - m)$ produces output $y(n - m)$.

In Chapter 2 we saw that an analog LTIS can be characterized by an impulse response or a differential equation. In this chapter we will develop a similar dual view, starting with the digital version of the impulse response

4.2.1 Digital LTIS Impulse Response

A digital LTIS can be completely characterized by its response to the digital impulse function $\delta(n)$. Let $h(n)$ be the *impulse response* of a digital LTIS, i.e., the output of the system when the input is $\delta(n)$. A more general input $x(n)$ can be defined as a summation of impulse functions as follows:

$$x(n) = \sum_{m=-\infty}^{\infty} \delta(n - m)x(m) \tag{4.11}$$

Since the system is time-invariant, the system response to $\delta(n - m)$ is $h(n - m)$ and thus, since the system is linear, the system response to $x(n)$ is

$$y(n) = \sum_{m=-\infty}^{\infty} h(n - m)x(m) \tag{4.12}$$

Equation (4.12), which is analogous to Equation (2.26), is called the *convolution* of $h(n)$ and $x(n)$ and is often written as $y(n) = h(n) * x(n)$. As in the analog case, it can easily be shown that convolution is associative, i.e.,

$$h(n) * x(n) = x(n) * h(n) \tag{4.13}$$

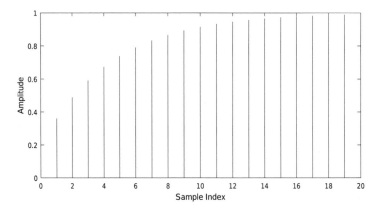

Figure 4.1: Unit step response of example LTIS ($\alpha = 0.8$).

We will reveal some other properties of convolution as we proceed.

Example 4.2.1. Consider a digital LTIS with an impulse response given by

$$h(n) = \alpha^n (1 - \alpha) u(n)$$

where $0 < \alpha < 1$ and $u(n)$ is the digital unit step function defined earlier. This is an example of a *causal* impulse response, in that $h(n)$ is zero for $n < 0$ so that the output is determined only by the current input and past inputs. Assume that the input is a unit step function, i.e.,

$$x(n) = u(n)$$

Determine the system output $y(n)$.

Solution The system output can be determined using Equation (4.12) as follows:

$$y(n) = \sum_{m=-\infty}^{\infty} h(n - m) x(m)$$

$$= \sum_{m=0}^{n} \alpha^{n-m} (1 - \alpha)$$

$$= \alpha^n (1 - \alpha) \sum_{m=0}^{n} \alpha^{-m}$$

$$= \alpha^n (1 - \alpha) \frac{\alpha^{-n} - \alpha}{1 - \alpha}$$

$$= 1 - \alpha^{n+1}$$

The output, shown in Figure 4.1, is a rising exponential.

In Example 4.2.1 both the input signal and the impulse response are causal, in that both are zero for $n < 0$. Although real signals have finite duration, it is useful to determine the response of a digital LTIS to the everlasting exponential $x(n) = z^n$ that is defined for all n. In this case the response is given by

$$y(n) = \sum_{m=-\infty}^{\infty} h(m)z^{n-m}$$

$$= z^n \sum_{m=-\infty}^{\infty} h(m)z^{-m}$$

$$= z^n H(z) \tag{4.14}$$

where

$$H(z) = \sum_{n=-\infty}^{\infty} h(n)z^{-n} \tag{4.15}$$

Here we have used the associative property of convolution. The response of a digital LTIS to the everlasting exponential input z^n is the input multiplied by a transfer function $H(z)$. This output of the LTIS is known as the *steady-state* response to the exponential input.

Example 4.2.2. Determine the transfer function corresponding to $h(n)$ in Example 4.2.1.

Solution Applying Equation (4.15) we have

$$H(z) = \sum_{n=-\infty}^{\infty} h(n)z^{-n}$$

$$= \sum_{n=0}^{\infty} \alpha^n (1-\alpha)z^{-n}$$

$$= (1-\alpha) \sum_{n=0}^{\infty} \left(\frac{\alpha}{z}\right)^n$$

$$= (1-\alpha)\frac{z}{z-\alpha}$$

4.2.2 LTIS Frequency Response

Consider a digital LTIS with transfer function $H(z)$ and a sinusoidal input $x(n) = e^{j\Omega n}$ (i.e., $z = e^{j\Omega}$). The output is given by

$$y(n) = H(e^{j\Omega})e^{j\Omega n} \tag{4.16}$$

which is a sinusoid with the same frequency as that of the input and a frequency-dependent complex amplitude. If $x(n)$ is a sampled analog sinusoid, then $\Omega = 2\pi f/f_s$. A plot of the magnitude and phase of H as a function of frequency is known as a frequency response plot.

Example 4.2.3. Plot the frequency response of the LTIS of Example 4.2.2.

Solution We can use the MATLAB function `freqz` (the discrete-time version of `freqs`) to plot the frequency response. First we rewrite $H(z)$ in a slightly different form.

$$H(z) = \frac{1 - \alpha}{1 - \alpha z^{-1}}$$

This is an example of a general class of transfer functions of the form

$$H(z) = \frac{b_0 + b_1 z^{-1} + \cdots + b_{N-1} z^{-(N-1)}}{a_0 + a_1 z^{-1} + \cdots + a_{M-1} z^{-(M-1)}}$$

In this example, $N = 1$, $M = 2$, and the coefficients are $b_0 = 1 - \alpha$, $a_0 = 1$, and $a_1 = -\alpha$. The following MATLAB script produces the desired plot.

```
alpha=0.8;
b=1-alpha;
a=[1 -alpha];
[h,w]=freqz(b,a);
plot(w,20*log10(abs(h)))
set(gca,'XTick',[0,pi/4,pi/2,3*pi/4,pi])
set(gca,'XTickLabel',{'0','\pi/4','\pi/2','3\pi/4','\pi'});
title('Frequency Response Plot')
xlabel('Frequency in Radians/Sample')
ylabel('Magnitude in dB')
```

The inputs to `freqz` are an array of the numerator coefficients `b` and an array of the denominator coefficients `a`. These arrays are set up in the first three lines of the script. `freqz` returns the complex frequency response for 200 (a default value that can be changed with an additional input) uniformly spaced frequencies in the array `h`. The corresponding frequencies in radians/sample are returned in the array `w`. The remaining lines of the script create a plot of the magnitude of the frequency response in decibels as a function of frequency. The script is designed to label the ticks on the x-axis using the symbol π. Note that the frequency ranges from 0 to π rad/s; the corresponding range in hertz is from 0 to $f_s/2$.

4.2.3   The z-Transform

When we considered the response of a digital LTIS to an everlasting exponential, we found that the output was the everlasting exponential multiplied by a transfer function $H(z)$ given by Equation (4.15). The transfer function $H(z)$ is an example of the *bilateral z-transform*, which, for a general digital signal $x(n)$, is defined by

$$X(z) = \sum_{n=-\infty}^{\infty} x(n) z^{-n} \tag{4.17}$$

Example 4.2.4. Determine the z-transform of the unit step signal $u(n)$.

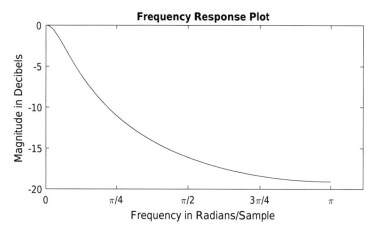

Figure 4.2: Frequency response of example LTIS ($\alpha = 0.8$).

$x(n)$	$X(z)$
$\delta(n-k)$	z^{-k}
$u(n)$	$\dfrac{z}{z-1}$
$\alpha^n u(n)$	$\dfrac{z}{z-\alpha}$

Table 4.1: A few z-transform pairs.

Solution

$$
\begin{aligned}
U(z) &= \sum_{n=-\infty}^{\infty} u(n) z^{-n} \\
&= \sum_{n=0}^{\infty} z^{-n} \\
&= \frac{z}{z-1}
\end{aligned}
$$

The combination of $x(n)$ and its z-transform $X(z)$ is called a z-transform pair. Table 4.1 lists a few z-transform pairs, and more comprehensive tables are widely available.

If we apply the z-transform to Equation (4.12) we have

$$Y(z) = \sum_{n=-\infty}^{\infty} y(n)z^{-n} = \sum_{n=-\infty}^{\infty} \sum_{m=-\infty}^{\infty} h(n-m)x(m)z^{-n}$$

$$= \sum_{m=-\infty}^{\infty} x(m)z^{-m} \sum_{n=-\infty}^{\infty} h(n-m)z^{-(n-m)}$$

$$= \sum_{m=-\infty}^{\infty} x(m)z^{-m} \sum_{n=-\infty}^{\infty} h(n)z^{-n}$$

$$= H(z)X(z) \tag{4.18}$$

Thus, the z-transform of the output of a digital LTIS is the product of the z-transforms of the impulse response and the input. This result is an example of the discrete-time version of the convolution theorem, which in general states that the z-transform of the convolution of two signals is the product of the z-transforms of the two signals.

Example 4.2.5. Solve Example 4.2.1 by the z-transform method.

Solution From Example 4.2.2 we know that

$$H(z) = \frac{(1-\alpha)z}{z-\alpha}$$

and from Table 4.1 we know that

$$X(z) = \frac{z}{z-1}$$

Thus, the z-transform of the output is given by

$$Y(z) = H(z)X(z)$$

$$= \frac{(1-\alpha)z}{z-\alpha}\frac{z}{z-1}$$

To determine the output $y(n)$ we need to find the *inverse* z-transform of $Y(z)$. The general formula for the inverse z-transform involves integration in the complex plane. However, in this case we can expand $Y(z)$ into partial fractions of the form

$$Y(z) = \frac{Az}{z-\alpha} + \frac{Bz}{z-1}$$

We can determine the values of A and B as follows:

$$A = (z-\alpha)Y(z)/z|_{z=\alpha} = -\alpha$$
$$B = (z-1)Y(z)/z|_{z=1} = 1$$

Thus, $Y(z)$ becomes

$$Y(z) = \frac{z}{z-1} - \alpha\frac{z}{z-\alpha}$$

Now we can use Table 4.1 to find the inverse transform.

$$y(n) = u(n) - \alpha\alpha^n u(n)$$
$$= (1-\alpha^{n+1})u(n)$$

which is identical to the result of Example 4.2.1.

4.2.4 Difference Equation Model

We have seen that a digital LTIS can be completely specified by its impulse response $h(n)$. In this section we will look at a class of digital LTIS characterized by a linear difference equation of the form

$$\sum_{m=0}^{M} a_m y(n-m) = \sum_{m=0}^{N} b_m x(n-m) \tag{4.19}$$

The coefficients a_m and b_m are called the feedback and feed-forward coefficients, respectively, and M and N are the feedback and feed-forward order, respectively. Equation (4.19) relates the system's output $y(n)$ to its current input $x(n)$, past inputs, and past outputs. To show this more explicitly we can rewrite Equation (4.19) as

$$y(n) = -\sum_{m=1}^{M} a_m y(n-m) + \sum_{m=0}^{N} b_m x(n-m) \tag{4.20}$$

where we have assumed $a_0 = 1$ without loss of generality. Equation (4.20) is one of the standard forms for a digital LTIS and can be used to calculate the system output recursively from the input and previous outputs. It is implemented in the MATLAB function `filter`.

Example 4.2.6. A digital LTIS is characterized by the following difference equation

$$y(n) = \alpha y(n-1) + (1-\alpha)x(n)$$

Determine the output of this LTIS for $x(n) = u(n)$.

Solution The MATLAB `filter` function requires three inputs: an array b of the coefficients b_m, an array a of the coefficients a_m, and an array u containing the input samples. The following is a suitable script to plot the LTIS output:

```
alpha=0.8;
b=1-alpha;
a=[1 -alpha];
u=ones(1,21);
y=filter(b,a,u);
stem(0:20,y,'Marker','none')
xlabel('Sample_Index')
ylabel('Amplitude')
```

Like similar scripts presented in previous examples, this script begins by setting up the required arrays, in this case the inputs for the `filter` function. The `filter` function computes the output y. The remainder of the script creates a plot of the result. The `stem` plotting routine is often more suitable for discrete-time signals. When used as in this example, the `filter` function assumes no prior input or initial output values. Figure 4.3 shows the output, which is identical to that of Example 4.2.1.

We can determine the impulse response for a digital LTIS characterized by Equation (4.20) by letting $x(n) = \delta(n)$ and solving the equation either analytically or numerically.

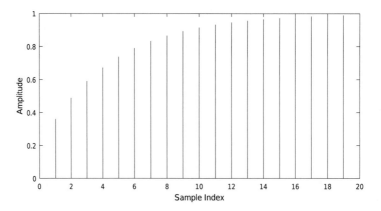

Figure 4.3: LTIS output for Example 4.2.6 ($\alpha = 0.8$).

Example 4.2.7. Determine the impulse response for the system in Example 4.2.6.

Solution The analytic solution to the difference equation is straightforward:

$$h(0) = 1 - \alpha$$
$$h(1) = \alpha(1 - \alpha)$$
$$h(2) = \alpha^2(1 - \alpha)$$
$$\vdots$$
$$h(n) = \alpha^n(1 - \alpha)$$

We can also calculate and plot $h(n)$ using a modification of the script from Example 4.2.6.

```
alpha=0.8;
b=1-alpha;
a=[1 -alpha];
d=zeros(1,21); d(1)=1;
h=filter(b,a,d);
stem(0:20,h,'Marker','none')
xlabel('Sample_Index')
ylabel('Amplitude')
```

The result of the MATLAB computation is shown in Figure 4.4.

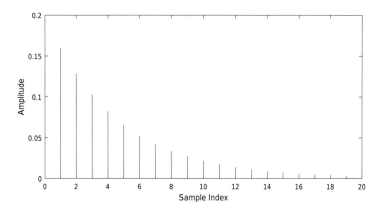

Figure 4.4: LTIS impulse response for Example 4.2.7 ($\alpha = 0.8$).

Now let us consider the z-transform of Equation (4.19):

$$\sum_{n=-\infty}^{\infty} \sum_{m=0}^{M} a_m y(n-m)z^{-n} = \sum_{n=-\infty}^{\infty} \sum_{m=0}^{N} b_m x(n-m)z^{-n}$$

$$\sum_{m=0}^{M} a_m z^{-m} \sum_{n=-\infty}^{\infty} y(n-m)z^{-(n-m)} = \sum_{m=0}^{N} b_m z^{-m} \sum_{n=-\infty}^{\infty} x(n-m)z^{-(n-m)}$$

$$\left(\sum_{m=0}^{M} a_m z^{-m} \right) Y(z) = \left(\sum_{m=0}^{N} b_m z^{-m} \right) X(z) \qquad (4.21)$$

This leads directly to the transfer function $H(z)$, which is the z-transform of the impulse response.

$$H(z) = \frac{Y(z)}{X(z)} = \frac{\sum_{m=0}^{N} b_m z^{-m}}{\sum_{m=0}^{M} a_m z^{-m}} \qquad (4.22)$$

Thus, there is a clear and straightforward correspondence between the difference equation model and the impulse response model.

Example 4.2.8. Determine $H(z)$ for the system of Example 4.2.6.

Solution By inspection of the difference equation

$$a_0 = 1$$
$$a_1 = -\alpha$$
$$b_0 = 1 - \alpha$$

Thus, $H(z)$ is given by

$$H(z) = \frac{1 - \alpha}{1 - \alpha z^{-1}}$$

4.2.5 Poles and Zeros

The transfer function $H(z)$ can also be expressed as[1]

$$H(z) = G \frac{(1 - q_1 z^{-1})(1 - q_2 z^{-1}) \cdots (1 - q_N z^{-1})}{(1 - p_1 z^{-1})(1 - p_2 z^{-1}) \cdots (1 - p_M z^{-1})} \qquad (4.23)$$

where the q and p coefficients are called the *poles* and *zeros*, respectively, of the transfer function, and G is a gain factor. Poles and zeros may be real or complex (the complex ones come in conjugate pairs) and their relation to the a and b coefficients is a matter of classic algebra.

It is easy to see that for the transfer function $H(z)$ in Example 4.2.8, $G = 1 - \alpha$ and there is a pole given by $p_1 = \alpha$. For higher-order transfer functions we can turn to MATLAB, which provides functions for computing and plotting poles and zeros.

Example 4.2.9. Calculate and plot the poles and zeros for the following transfer function:

$$H(z) = \frac{1/6 + (1/2)z^{-1} + (1/2)z^{-2} + (1/6)z^{-3}}{1 + (1/3)z^{-2}}$$

Solution We can calculate the poles and zeros using the MATLAB function `tf2zpk`

b=[1/6 0.5 0.5 1/6];
a=[1 0 1/3 0];
[z,p,k]=tf2zpk(b,a);

The resulting zeros, poles, and gain factor are:

z =
    -1.0000 + 0.0000 i
    -1.0000 + 0.0000 i
    -1.0000 - 0.0000 i
p =
     0.0000 + 0.0000 i
     0.0000 + 0.5774 i
     0.0000 - 0.5774 i
k =
     0.1667

We can plot the poles and zeros using the MATLAB function `zplane`, which accepts either the column vectors **z** and **p** or the row vectors **b** and **a** as input. In the plot shown in Figure 4.5 the locations of the poles and zeros are noted with × and ○, respectively.

Note that the pole-zero plot in Figure 4.5 includes the unit circle, which corresponds to $z = e^{-j\Omega}$. If we make this substitution into Equation (4.23) we obtain an alternate form of the frequency response function $H(j\Omega)$:

$$H(j\Omega) = G \frac{(1 - q_1 e^{-j\Omega})(1 - q_2 e^{-j\Omega}) \cdots (1 - q_N e^{-j\Omega})}{(1 - p_1 e^{-j\Omega})(1 - p_2 e^{-j\Omega}) \cdots (1 - p_M e^{-j\Omega})} \qquad (4.24)$$

---

[1]A similar expression applies to the analog transfer function $H(s)$.

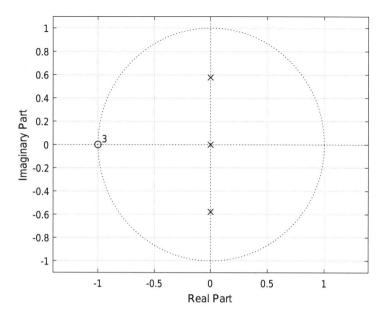

Figure 4.5: Pole-zero plot for Example 4.2.9.

The magnitude of the frequency response is given by

$$|H(j\Omega)| = |G|\frac{|1 - q_1 e^{-j\Omega}||1 - q_2 e^{-j\Omega}|\cdots|1 - q_N e^{-j\Omega}|}{|1 - p_1 e^{-j\Omega}||1 - p_2 e^{-j\Omega}|\cdots|1 - p_M e^{-j\Omega}|}$$

$$= |G||e^{-j(N-M)\Omega}|\frac{|e^{j\Omega} - q_1||e^{j\Omega} - q_2|\cdots|e^{j\Omega} - q_N|}{|e^{j\Omega} - p_1||e^{j\Omega} - p_2|\cdots|e^{j\Omega} - p_M|}$$

$$= |G|\frac{|e^{j\Omega} - q_1||e^{j\Omega} - q_2|\cdots|e^{j\Omega} - q_N|}{|e^{j\Omega} - p_1||e^{j\Omega} - p_2|\cdots|e^{j\Omega} - p_M|} \tag{4.25}$$

Thus, each pole and zero contributes a factor to the magnitude of the frequency response equal to the distance between that pole or zero and the point $z = e^{j\Omega}$.

Example 4.2.10. Figure 4.6 is a pole-zero plot of $H(z) = (1 - \alpha)/(1 - \alpha z^{-1})$ for $\alpha = 0.5$. There is a zero at $z = 0$ and a pole at $z = 0.5$. The lines connect the pole and the zero to a point on the unit circle. The magnitude of the frequency response is proportional to the ratio of the lengths of these two lines and thus varies as $1/d_1$. As we move the point counterclockwise around the unit circle, d_1 increases from a minimum of $1 - \alpha$ to a maximum of $1 + \alpha$.

Example 4.2.10 shows how we can determine the magnitude of the frequency response (except for the gain factor) from a pole-zero plot of the transfer function. We can also determine the frequency-dependent component of the phase, which is given by

$$\angle H(j\Omega) = \angle G + (N - M)\Omega + \sum_{n=1}^{N} \angle(e^{j\Omega} - q_n) - \sum_{m=1}^{M} \angle(e^{j\Omega} - p_m) \tag{4.26}$$

In Example 4.2.10, $\angle G = 0$ and $N = M$ so that the total phase is simply $\Omega - \phi_1$.

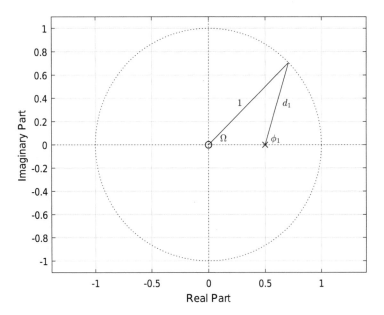

Figure 4.6: Determining frequency response from a pole-zero plot.

4.3 Fourier Analysis of Digital Signals and Systems

In Chapter 2 we learned about the Fourier series and Fourier transform for analog signals. Fourier analysis is also applicable to digital signals and systems. This section introduces the basic tools for obtaining the frequency domain representation of digital signals and for frequency domain signal processing.

4.3.1 Discrete-Time Fourier Series

A periodic digital signal can be expanded in a digital version of the Fourier series as

$$x(n) = \sum_{m=-\infty}^{\infty} c_m e^{jm\Omega_0 n} \tag{4.27}$$

where $\Omega_0 = 2\pi/N_0$ and N_0 is the period in samples. However, the digital version reduces to a finite sum as follows:

$$x(n) = \sum_{k=0}^{N_0-1} \sum_{l=-\infty}^{\infty} c_{k+lN_0} e^{j(k+lN_0)\Omega_0 n}$$

$$= \sum_{k=0}^{N_0-1} e^{jk\Omega_0 n} \sum_{l=-\infty}^{\infty} c_{k+lN_0}$$

$$= \sum_{k=0}^{N_0-1} d_k e^{jk\Omega_0 n} \tag{4.28}$$

It can be shown that

$$d_k = \frac{1}{N_0} \sum_{n=0}^{N_0-1} x(n)e^{-jk\Omega_0 n} \tag{4.29}$$

for $k = 0, 1, \ldots, N_0 - 1$. Equations 4.28 and 4.29 define the *discrete-time Fourier series* (DTFS) representation of the periodic signal $x(n)$. They are very similar to the pair of equations known as the *discrete Fourier transform* (DFT). The DFT equations are

$$X(k) = \sum_{n=0}^{N_0-1} x(n)e^{-jk\Omega_0 n} \tag{4.30}$$

$$x(n) = \frac{1}{N_0} \sum_{k=0}^{N_0-1} X(k)e^{jk\Omega_0 n} \tag{4.31}$$

where $X(k)$ is the DFT of $x(n)$ and $x(n)$ is the inverse DFT (or IDFT) of $X(k)$. Straightforward calculation of $X(k)$ using Equation (4.30) requires on the order of N_0^2 calculations, which can prohibitive for large values of N_0. However, both the DFT and the IDFT can be evaluated very efficiently using an algorithm known as the fast Fourier transform (FFT) [1]. This algorithm is implemented in MATLAB as the functions `fft` and `ifft`. Thus we can use the FFT to compute $X(k)$ and obtain the DTFS coefficients as $d_k = X(k)/N_0$. We will say more about the DFT later in this chapter.

Each coefficient d_k of the DTFS has a corresponding frequency $k\Omega_0$ and is thus called a frequency component of the signal $x(n)$. The frequencies range from 0 to $2\pi(N_0-1)/N_0$ (not quite 2π). Taken together, the frequency components define the frequency domain representation of $x(n)$ and a plot of the components vs. frequency is the *Fourier spectrum* of $x(n)$.

It turns out that some of the frequency components are redundant. It can be easily shown that

$$d_{N_0-k} = d_k^* \tag{4.32}$$

so that if we know $d_0 \cdots d_{N_0/2}$ (assuming that N_0 is even), we can calculate the remaining coefficients. Thus, it is common to consider only the first half (roughly) of the frequency range. Note that the frequency corresponding to coefficient index $N_0/2$ is π radians per sample, which corresponds to the Nyquist frequency $f_s/2$.

Example 4.3.1. Compute the coefficients of the DTFS of a discrete-time square wave with $N_0 = 64$ and the base period defined by

$$x(n) = \begin{cases} 1 & n = 0, 1, \ldots, 31 \\ -1 & n = 32, 33, \ldots, 63 \end{cases}$$

Plot the magnitudes of the components. Note that $x(n)$ can be viewed as samples of a continuous-time square wave $x(t)$.

Solution The following MATLAB script produces the desired result:

```
N0=64;
x=[ones(1,N0/2) -ones(1,N0/2)];
```

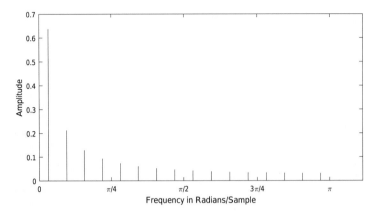

Figure 4.7: Fourier spectrum for Example 4.3.1.

```
d=fft(x)/N0;
Omega0=2*pi/N0;
Omega=(0:N0/2)*Omega0;
stem(Omega,abs(d(1:N0/2+1)),'marker','none');
set(gca,'XTick',[0,pi/4,pi/2,3*pi/4,pi])
set(gca,'XTickLabel',{'0','\pi/4','\pi/2','3\pi/4','\pi'});
xlabel('Frequency in Radians/Sample');
ylabel('Amplitude');
```

Most of the script is devoted to producing a nicely labeled plot of the spectrum. The real work is done in the third line of the script, which invokes the **fft** function provided by MATLAB in order to compute the DTFS coefficients (note division by N_0). Figure 4.7 shows the resulting plot.

Unsurprisingly, the DTFS is an approximation of the Fourier series representation of a periodic continuous-time signal. Starting with Equation (2.20) for the coefficients of the complex exponential form of the continuous-time Fourier series (CTFS), we have (changing notation a bit)

$$C_k = \frac{1}{T} \int_0^T x(t)e^{-jk\omega_0 t}dt$$

$$\approx \frac{1}{T} \sum_{n=0}^{N_0-1} x(n)e^{-jk\omega_0 n\tau_s}\tau_s$$

$$= \frac{1}{N_0} \sum_{n=0}^{N_0-1} x(n)e^{-jk\Omega_0 n} = d_k \qquad (4.33)$$

where $x(n)$ is the sampled version of $x(t)$ and τ_s is the sampling interval. Thus, we can use the DTFS (and thus the FFT) to approximate the Fourier series representation of an analog signal.

Example 4.3.2. Compare the DTFS from Example 4.3.1 with the CTFS of the corresponding continuous-time signal.

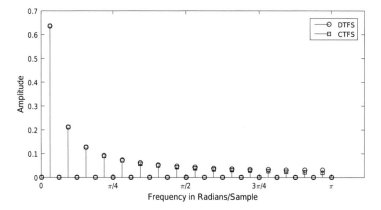

Figure 4.8: DTFS/CTFS comparison (Example 4.3.2).

Solution The magnitudes of the CTFS coefficients are

$$|C_k| = \begin{cases} 0 & k \text{ even} \\ \dfrac{2}{\pi k} & k \text{ odd} \end{cases}$$

Figure 4.8 displays the DTFS coefficients with the corresponding CTFS coefficients. There is good agreement up to about one half the Nyquist frequency.

Although there are only N_0 unique values of d_k, Equation (4.29) defines d_k for any value of k. The resulting extended spectrum turns out to be N_0-periodic just like $x(n)$.

Note that the DTFS coefficients can be determined from any N_0 elements of a periodic signal $x(n)$:

$$\sum_{n=m}^{m+N_0-1} x(n)e^{-jk\Omega_0 n} = \sum_{n=m}^{N_0-1} x(n)e^{-jk\Omega_0 n} + \sum_{n=N_0}^{m+N_0-1} x(n)e^{-jk\Omega_0 n}$$

$$= \sum_{n=m}^{N_0-1} x(n)e^{-jk\Omega_0 n} + \sum_{n=0}^{m-1} x(n+N_0)e^{-jk\Omega_0 (n+N_0)}$$

$$= \sum_{n=m}^{N_0-1} x(n)e^{-jk\Omega_0 n} + \sum_{n=0}^{m-1} x(n)e^{-jk\Omega_0 n}$$

$$= d_k \tag{4.34}$$

4.3.2   Discrete-Time Fourier Transform

Even if $x(n)$ is not periodic we can still calculate its Fourier spectrum. The *discrete-time Fourier transform* (DTFT) and its inverse are defined as follows:

$$X(\Omega) = \sum_{n=-\infty}^{\infty} x(n)e^{-j\Omega n} \tag{4.35}$$

$$x(n) = \int_{2\pi} X(\Omega)e^{jk\Omega}d\Omega \tag{4.36}$$

where $\int_{2\pi}$ is the integral over any continuous interval of length 2π. Note that the DTFT is just the z-transform with $z = e^{j\Omega}$.

Whereas the frequency components of the DTFS are defined for only discrete frequencies ($\Omega = k\Omega_0$), the DTFT is a continuous function of Ω. Also, it is easy to show that the DTFT is a periodic function of Ω with period 2π. And the DTFT has the conjugate symmetry property, i.e.,

$$X(-\Omega) = X^*(\Omega) \tag{4.37}$$

Finally, the convolution theorem applies to te DTFT, i.e., the DTFT of $x(n) * y(n)$ is $X(\Omega)Y(\Omega)$.

Example 4.3.3. Determine the DTFT $X(\Omega)$ of the signal $x(n) = \alpha^n u(n)$. Plot the magnitude of $X(\Omega)$ for $0 \leq \Omega \leq \pi$.

Solution The DTFT is given by

$$X(\Omega) = \sum_{n=0}^{\infty} \alpha^n e^{-j\Omega n}$$

$$= \sum_{n=0}^{\infty} (\alpha e^{-j\Omega})^n$$

$$= \frac{1}{1 - \alpha e^{-j\Omega}}$$

which can also be obtained by substituting $z = e^{j\Omega}$ into the z-transform of $x(n)$ listed in Table 4.1. The following MATLAB script produces the plot shown in Figure 4.9:

```
alpha=0.8;
N=100;
Omega=linspace(0,pi,N);
X=1./(1-alpha*exp(-1j*Omega));
plot(Omega,abs(X))
set(gca,'XTick',[0,pi/4,pi/2,3*pi/4,pi])
set(gca,'XTickLabel',{'0','\pi/4','\pi/2','3\pi/4','\pi'});
title('Frequency_Response_Plot')
xlabel('Frequency_in_Radians/Sample')
ylabel('Magnitude')
```

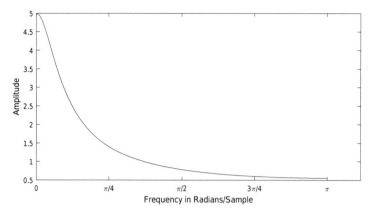

Figure 4.9: DTFT for Example 4.3.3.

4.3.3 DFT

Let $x(n)$ be a finite duration signal with length N_0 (i.e., $x(n)$ is defined for $n = 0, 1, \ldots, N_0 - 1$). Then the DTFT of $x(n)$ is given by

$$X(\Omega) = \sum_{n=0}^{N_0-1} x(n)e^{-j\Omega n} \tag{4.38}$$

If we sample the DTFT at frequencies of the form $\Omega = k\Omega_0 = 2\pi k/N_0$ we have

$$X(k\Omega_0) = \sum_{n=0}^{N_0-1} x(n)e^{-jk\Omega_0 n}$$
$$= X(k) \tag{4.39}$$

which is the DFT of $x(n)$. As we saw in Section 4.3.1, $d_k = X(k)/N_0$ is the kth frequency component of a *periodic extension* $x_{N_0}(n)$ of $x(n)$ (i.e., $x(n)$ is one period of $x_{N_0}(n)$). Thus, the DTFS representation of $x_{N_0}(n)$ is given by

$$x_{N_0}(n) = \frac{1}{N_0} \sum_{k=0}^{N_0-1} X(k)e^{jk\Omega_0 n} \tag{4.40}$$

which is the IDFT of $X(k)$. For $n = 0, 1, \ldots, N_0 - 1$, $x_{N_0}(n)$ is identical to $x(n)$ so that a finite duration digital signal can be represented by and recovered from its DFT.

As we will see, the DFT, which can be computed very efficiently with the FFT algorithm, is a very useful tool for audio signal processing. It is worth noting a few more basic properties of the DFT at this point:

Frequency range: The frequency corresponding to $X(k)$ is $k\Omega_0$ radians/sample, which corresponds to $\omega_k = k\Omega_0 f_s$ radians/s or $f_k = k f_s/N_0$ Hz. Thus, the frequencies range from $f_0 = 0$ to $f_{N_0-1} = (N_0 - 1)f_s/N_0$ Hz.

Conjugate symmetry: For any value of k, $X(N_0 - k) = X^*(k)$. This means that the DFT is completely determined by components $X(0)$ through $X(N_0/2)$ (assuming N_0 is even).

Parseval's theorem: The DFT version of Parseval's theorem is

$$\sum_{n=0}^{N_0} |x(n)|^2 = \frac{1}{N} \sum_{k=0}^{N-1} |X(k)|^2 \qquad (4.41)$$

4.3.4 Interim Summary

At this point we have introduced three different but related Fourier representations of digital signals:

- Discrete-time Fourier series (DTFS): a Fourier series representation of a periodic digital signal; defines the signal as the sum of a finite number of sinusoidal components at harmonically related discrete frequencies.

- Discrete-time Fourier transform (DTFT): a Fourier integral representation of an aperiodic digital signal; defines the signal as the integral of a continuum of sinusoidal components covering a continuous range of frequencies.

- Discrete Fourier transform (DFT): a transform that maps a finite duration digital signal into a finite number of sinusoidal components at harmonically related discrete frequencies; can be used to calculate both the DTFS and samples of the DTFT.

It may be appropriate, therefore, to regard the DFT (and thus the FFT) as a tool for performing Fourier analysis of both periodic and aperiodic signals.

4.3.5 Circular Convolution

Let $x(n)$ and $y(n)$ be two periodic digital signals with period N_0. The circular convolution of $x(n)$ and $y(n)$ is defined by

$$x(n) \circledast y(n) = \sum_{m=0}^{N_0-1} x(n-m)y(m) = \sum_{m=0}^{N_0-1} y(n-m)x(m) \qquad (4.42)$$

If we take the DFT of both sides of Equation (4.43) (selecting, without loss of generality, the second version), we have

$$\sum_{n=0}^{N_0-1} x(n) \circledast y(n)e^{-jk\Omega_0 n} = \sum_{n=0}^{N_0-1}\sum_{m=0}^{N_0-1} y(n-m)x(m)e^{-jk\Omega_0 n}$$

$$= \sum_{m=0}^{N_0-1}\sum_{n=0}^{N_0-1} x(m)e^{-jk\Omega_0 m}y(n-m)e^{-jk\Omega_0(n-m)}$$

$$= \sum_{m=0}^{N_0-1} x(m)e^{-jk\Omega_0 m} \sum_{n=0}^{N_0-1} y(n-m)e^{-jk\Omega_0(n-m)}$$

$$= X(k)Y(k) \qquad (4.43)$$

Here we have used the fact that the DFT of a periodic signal can be computed using any N_0 consecutive signal values. Equation (4.43) is a version of the convolution theorem stating that the DFT of the circular convolution of two periodic digital signals with identical periods is the product of the DFTs of the signals, where the signal DFTs are computed from one period of the signals.

Now consider the linear convolution of a signal $x(n)$ with finite duration N_x and an impulse response $h(n)$ with finite duration N_h.

$$y(n) = h(n) * x(n) = \sum_{m=0}^{n} h(n-m)x(m) \qquad (4.44)$$

where $h(n) = 0$ for $n < 0$ and $n \geq N_h$ and $x(n) = 0$ for $n < 0$ and $n \geq N_x$. The result $y(n)$ is nonzero for $n = 0, 1, \ldots, N_h + N_x - 2$. Unfortunately the DFT of $y(n)$ is not equal to the product of the DFTs of $h(n)$ and $x(n)$ in this case. In fact, the DFTs are of unequal length! So how can we use the DFT (sped up by the FFT) as a practical approach to evaluating Equation (4.44)? The answer is to pad $h(n)$ and $x(n)$ with zeros so that both have length $N_h + N_x - 1$, i.e., append $N_x - 1$ zeros to $h(n)$ and $N_h - 1$ zeros to $x(n)$. The circular convolution of the padded versions of $h(n)$ and $x(n)$ is identical to the linear convolution of the unpadded versions.

Example 4.3.4. A digital LTIS has a finite impulse response given by

$$h(n) = \begin{cases} \alpha^n(1-\alpha) & n = 0, 1, \ldots, N_h - 1 \\ 0 & \text{otherwise} \end{cases}$$

Determine the output of this system in reponse to a unit pulse of length N_x samples.

Solution The following MATLAB script computes and plots the response using two approaches:

- Use the MATLAB function **conv** to compute the response by linear convolution.

- Use the MATLAB functions **fft** and **ifft** to compute the response by circular convolution.

```
Nx=25;
Nh=15;
Ny=Nx+Nh−1;
x=ones(1,Nx);
h=zeros(1,Nh);
alpha=0.8;
for  n=1:Nh
     h(n)=(1−alpha)*alpha^n;
end
y1=conv(h,x);
y2=ifft(fft(h,Ny).*fft(x,Ny));
subplot(2,1,1);  stem(y1,'marker','none');
title('Convolution␣Method')
xlabel('Sample␣Index')
ylabel('Sample␣Value')
```

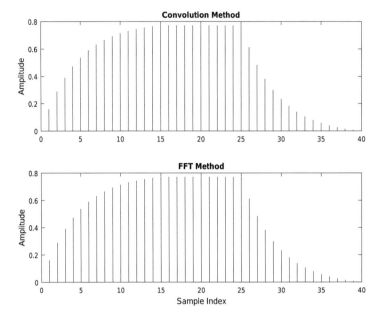

Figure 4.10: Results for Example 4.3.4.

```
subplot(2,1,2); stem(y2,'marker','none');
title('FFT_Method')
xlabel('Sample_Index')
ylabel('Sample_Value')
```

Computing the response by linear convolution is straightforward. For circular convolution, we first have to compute the common length $N_y = N_h + N_x$. The `fft` function adjusts both the impulse response and the input to this length by zero-padding. Note that the MATLAB operator `.*` indicates component-by-component multiplication. Figure 4.10 shows the plots produced by this script. The results appear identical for the two methods.

Although the FFT method seems more complex, it is much faster than straightforward convolution for large values of N_x or N_h.[2]

4.3.6   Fast Convolution of Long Signals

In many practical situations the length of the input signal N_x is so large that the signal must be processed in blocks. In the case of a real-time signal, N_x may even be unknown, leaving block processing as the only option. This section presents the *overlap-add* method for convolving such a signal with a finite impulse response $h(n)$.

---

[2]The MATLAB `conv` function used in the example does not necessarily use straightforward convolution.

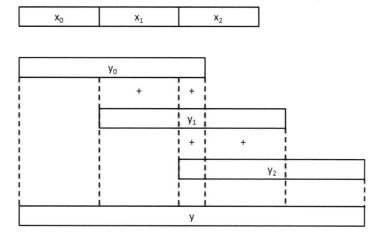

Figure 4.11: Illustration of overlap-add convolution.

We begin by expressing the input signal $x(n)$ as a summation of blocks of length L.

$$x(n) = \sum_{k=0}^{K-1} x_k(n - kL) \tag{4.45}$$

where

$$x_k(n) = \begin{cases} x(n+kL) & n = 0, 1, \ldots, L-1 \\ 0 & \text{otherwise} \end{cases} \tag{4.46}$$

and K is the number of blocks (with zero-padding on the last block, if necessary). Since convolution is a linear operation, we have

$$\begin{aligned} h(n) * x(n) &= \sum_{k=0}^{K-1} h(n) * x_k(n - kL) \\ &= \sum_{k=0}^{K-1} y_k(n - kL) \end{aligned} \tag{4.47}$$

The kth block consists of L consecutive signal components starting at $n = kL$. The kth output block consists of $L + M - 1$ consecutive signal components (M is the length of $h(n)$) and also starts at $n = kL$. Figure 4.11 illustrates how the output blocks are summed to obtain the final result (in this illustration $K = 3$). Each output component is the convolution of the corresponding input component with the impulse response. The overall output is the sum of the components as indicated in the figure. Note that each block-processing step produces L final outputs and contributes to producing subsequent outputs.

The following MATLAB function implements the block-processing step of the overlap-add method:

```
function y=overlapAdd(x,h)
persistent L N buffer;
```

```
if  (isempty(buffer))
    L=length(x);
    N=2^nextpow2(L+length(h)-1);
    buffer=zeros(N,1);
end
buffer=buffer+ifft(fft(h,N).*fft(x,N));
y=buffer(1:L);
buffer=[buffer(L+1:N); zeros(L,1)];
```

This function produces a block of L values of $h(n) * x(n)$ based on a corresponding block of L values of $x(n)$, the entire impulse response $h(n)$, and a buffer of size $N \geq L + M - 1$. The code uses **persistent** variables that are set when the function is first called and retained until they are cleared using the MATLAB **clear** command (see MATLAB documentation for more information about persistent variables). The block size L, the buffer length N, and the buffer itself (**buffer**) are persistent variables. Note that the buffer size is adjusted upward to a power of 2. This adjustment improves the efficiency of the FFT algorithm without affecting the result.

4.4   Summary

As we will see throughout the remainder of this book, a digital LTIS can perform a variety of audio signal-processing functions including filtering, equalizing, and adding effects. Basic tools such as the FFT are available in several environments and can be used not only for study, but for practical implementation of audio signal-processing systems.

Exercises

1. An LTIS is defined by the following impulse response

$$h(n) = \begin{cases} 1 & n = 0 \\ \alpha^{n-1}(\alpha - 1) & n > 0 \end{cases}$$

   where $0 < \alpha < 1$. Show that if the input is a unit step function, then the output is given by $y(n) = \alpha^n u(n)$.

2. An LTIS is defined by the following impulse response

$$h(n) = \begin{cases} \dfrac{1}{N} & n = 0, 1, \ldots, N-1 \\ 0 & n \geq N \end{cases}$$

   Determine the output of this LTIS if the input is a unit step function.

3. Show that the transfer function $H(z)$ for the impulse response $h(n)$ in Exercise 1 is given by

$$H(z) = \frac{1 - z^{-1}}{1 - \alpha z^{-1}}$$

4. Using Table 4.1 and the results of Exercise 3, solve Exercise 1 using the z-transform method, i.e., calculate $Y(z) = H(z)U(z)$ and use the table to determine $y(n)$.

5. Determine a difference equation representation for the LTIS in Exercise 1.

MATLAB Projects

1. Using the MATLAB functions **freqz** and **zplane**, plot of the frequency response and the pole-zero plot for $H(z)$ in Exercise 3.

2. Plot the Fourier spectrum of a discrete-time sawtooth wave with $N_0 = 64$ and the base period defined by

$$x(n) = n/(N_0 - 1)$$

for $n = 0, 1, \ldots, N_0 - 1$.

Chapter 5

Spectral Analysis of Audio Signals

Besides being a useful tool for the analysis of LTIS, Fourier analysis (i.e., the DFT, etc.) provides an alternate representation of a signal. We originally defined a discrete-time signal as a sequence of signal values $x(n)$. We refer to this as the *time domain* representation of a signal, since each value corresponds to a point in time. Fourier analysis transforms the signal to a sequence of values $X(k)$, where each value corresponds to a frequency. Thus, we call $X(k)$ the *frequency domain* representation of the signal.

In this chapter we will examine the spectra of real audio signals, making extensive use of MATLAB. Some details on how to use MATLAB tools designed for this purpose are included.

5.1 Spectra of Signal Segments

In this section we will perform Fourier analyses of signals of relatively short duration that can be analyzed in their entirety rather than in blocks.

Figure 5.1 is a time domain plot of the sound of the A string of an acoustic guitar. The time domain representation shows that the signal has a duration of a bit more than 4 s, during which it initially decays rapidly, then maintains a steady amplitude for a second or so, and finally decays more or less linearly. Figure 5.2 provides a closer look at a segment of the signal. We can now see that the signal is somewhat periodic, and with some effort we could determine the fundamental frequency. But will another view tell us more about this signal?

Figure 5.3 is a plot of the magnitude of the DFT of the signal for frequencies up to the Nyquist frequency ($f_s/2$, where f_s is the sampling frequency). Figure 5.4 shows the spectrum through 2000 Hz. Closer inspection shows that the peaks in the spectrum are at multiples of 110 Hz. The amplitudes of these peaks tend to decrease with increasing frequency, but not consistently. The frequency domain view shows that the signal is mostly made up from sinusoidal components at frequencies that are multiples of the fundamental frequency of 110 Hz. This is in agreement with

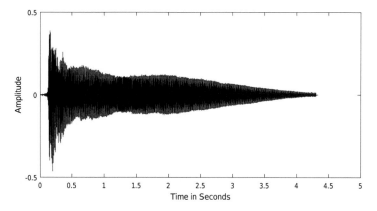

Figure 5.1: Acoustic guitar A string: time domain.

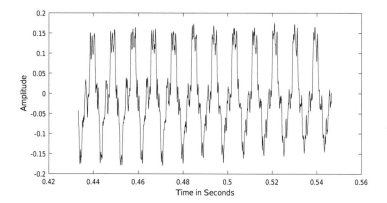

Figure 5.2: Acoustic guitar A string: time domain close-up.

the classic analysis of a vibrating string, which predicts that the string vibrates in a combination of harmonically related modes.

This example shows how Fourier analysis of a signal can expose important properties of a signal not readily evident in the time domain. Figures 5.5 and 5.6 show time and frequency domain views of a more complex signal – a C chord strummed on an acoustic guitar. The time domain view is not fundamentally different from the A string signal, but the frequency domain view clearly shows the more complex mix of frequency components associated with a chord produced by several vibrating strings with different fundamental frequencies and harmonics. The frequency domain plot is truncated at 3500 Hz, since harmonics above this frequency are relatively weak.

Figure 5.7 shows the lower portion of the spectrum of the acoustic guitar C chord shown in Figure 5.6. Each of the peaks above a certain threshold is annotated with the corresponding frequency with the name of the musical note associated with the frequency given in parentheses. Here it is assumed that the frequency associated with the nth semitone is given by

$$f_n = 440 \cdot 2^{n/12} \tag{5.1}$$

where $n = 0$ corresponds to middle A (negative values of n correspond to semitones

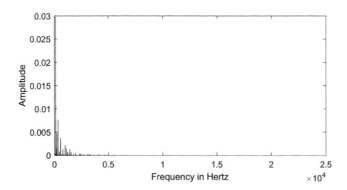

Figure 5.3: Acoustic guitar A string: frequency domain.

below middle A). We can invert Equation (5.1) to determine the note that most closely corresponds to a given frequency.

$$n = \text{round}[12 \log_2(f/440)] \qquad (5.2)$$

But we also want to convert n to one of the 12 note names listed in Table 5.1. For $n \geq 0$ this is straightforward – we simply calculate $n' = n \bmod 12$ and use n' as the index of a look-up table. The more general formula $n' = n - 12\lfloor n/12 \rfloor$ provides the desired result for both positive and negative n. The MATLAB function mod uses this formula.

In Figure 5.7 most of the prominent peaks correspond to the notes of the C major chord (C, E, and G). We also see a a peak at 587.8 Hz that most closely corresponds

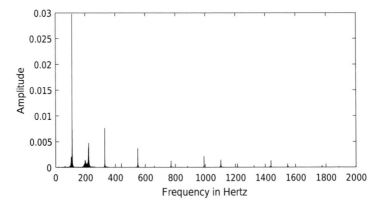

Figure 5.4: Acoustic guitar A string: frequency domain close-up.

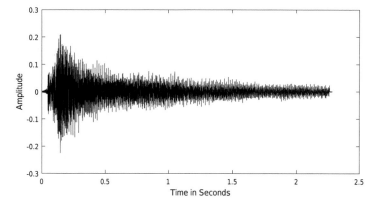

Figure 5.5: Guitar C chord: time domain.

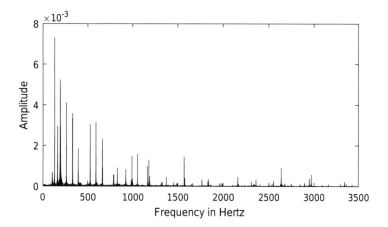

Figure 5.6: Guitar C chord: frequency domain.

to a D note. However, this frequency closely matches the third harmonic of the 194.9 Hz G note.

5.2 Spectral Analysis of Changing Sounds

Figures 5.8 and 5.9 show time and frequency domain views of the sound produced by strumming first a C chord and then a D chord on an acoustic guitar. It is clear from the time domain view that there are two separate sounds, one after the other. This is not at all evident in the frequency domain view, which contains frequency components from both chords and shows no variation with respect to time.

The *short-time Fourier transform* (STFT) provides a means to see how a signal varies with frequency *and* time. The basic idea of the STFT is to compute the DFT of successive blocks of signal data. We define the kth signal block as a vector, i.e.,

$$\mathbf{x}(k) = \begin{bmatrix} x(kM) & x(kM+1) & \cdots & x(kM+L-1) \end{bmatrix} \tag{5.3}$$

where L is the block length and M is the step size ($0 < M \le L$). For $M < L$

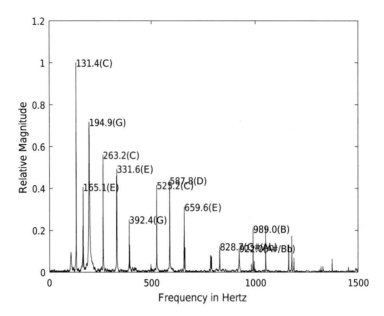

Figure 5.7: Guitar C chord spectrum with annotation.

Index	Note Name
0	A
1	A#/Bb
2	B
3	C
4	C#/Db
5	D
6	D#/Eb
7	E
8	F
9	F#/Gb
10	G
11	G#/Ab

Table 5.1: Look-up table for note names.

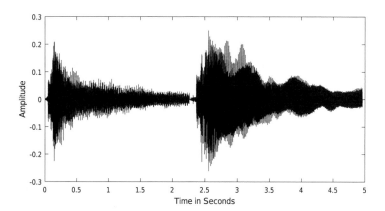

Figure 5.8: Guitar chord progression: time domain.

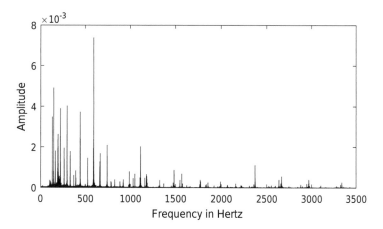

Figure 5.9: Guitar chord progression: frequency domain.

the blocks overlap by $L - M$ samples. Each signal block is associated with a time period of duration M/f_s starting at time kM/fs, where f_s is the sampling rate. For simplicity, however, we will associate the signal block with its center time. We can express the DFT as a function that maps a time domain signal vector $\mathbf{x}$ into a frequency domain signal vector $\mathbf{X}$, i.e.,

$$\mathbf{X} = \text{DFT}(\mathbf{x}) \tag{5.4}$$

Thus, the DFT of the kth signal block is given by

$$\mathbf{X}(k) = \text{DFT}[\mathbf{x}(k)] \tag{5.5}$$

Equation (5.5) provides L frequency components in the range $0 \le f \le f_s$ for each value of k. Thus, $\mathbf{X}(k)$ represents the signal as a function of both frequency and time. However, before declaring victory, we need to add a small modification. The DFT of a signal block may contain artifacts of its abrupt beginning and ending. Thus, it is useful to smooth the blocks by weighting the samples with a window function, such as the Hanning window defined by

$$w(n) = 0.5 \left(1 - \cos \frac{2\pi n}{L - 1} \right) \tag{5.6}$$

The smoothed block becomes

$$\mathbf{s}(k) = \mathbf{w} \cdot \mathbf{x}(k) \tag{5.7}$$

where $\mathbf{a} \cdot \mathbf{b}$ is a vector of the products of the elements of $\mathbf{a}$ and $\mathbf{b}$, i.e., the nth element of $\mathbf{a} \cdot \mathbf{b}$ is $a(n)b(n)$. The smoothed STFT becomes

$$\mathbf{S}(k) = \text{DFT}[\mathbf{s}(k)] \tag{5.8}$$

The MATLAB function `spectrogram` calculates the STFT of a signal. There are a number of ways to invoke `spectrogram`, including the following:

```
[s,f,t] = spectrogram(x,window,noverlap,nfft,fs);
```

The input arguments are:

x the signal vector

window either an integer specifying the block length (L in our notation) or a vector containing the window function. For integer input, `spectrogram` defaults to a Hamming window. For vector input, the block size is the length of the vector.

noverlap the number of overlap samples ($L - M$ in our notation)

nfft the number of DFT components to calculate for each block

fs the sampling rate in Hz

The Hamming window is a generalized version of the Hanning window given by

$$w(n) = 0.54 - 0.46 \cos \frac{2\pi n}{L - 1} \tag{5.9}$$

The `spectrogram` output arguments are:

s the STFT matrix with rows corresponding to normalized frequencies and columns corresponding to times

f a vector of `nfft/2+1` frequencies ranging linearly from 0 to $f_s/2$

t a time axis vector based on the center time of each block

The STFT matrix **s** contains one row for each element of **f** and one column for each element of **t**. If the output arguments are omitted, `spectrogram` plots the STFT. We can also use the MATLAB plotting function `surf`, giving us more control over the plot.

Figure 5.10 is a graphical rendering of the STFT of the guitar chord progression. The x-axis is time, the y-axis is frequency (limited to 1500 Hz in this example), and the magnitude (converted to decibels) of the STFT is indicated by the gray level (light areas correspond to larger amplitudes). Now we can see how the spectrum changes from that of the C chord to that of the D chord. Figure 5.11 shows the STFT of a song clip including vocal, acoustic guitar, and electric bass. The complete MATLAB script to create these plots is:

```
[x,fs]=audioread('<file_name>');
window 2048;
noverlap=window/2;
nfft=window;
[s,f,t]=spectrogram(x,window,noverlap,nfft,fs);
fmax=1500;
N1=round(2*fmax*length(f)/fs);
surf(t,f(1:N1),20*log10(abs(s(1:N1,:))),'edgecolor','none');
axis tight
colormap gray
view(2)
pbaspect([2 1 1])
xlabel('Time_in_Seconds')
ylabel('Frequency_in_Hz')
```

If the `colormap` statement is omitted, MATLAB defaults to color display of the amplitude. Note that the amplitude is converted to decibels.

Can we recover the original signal $x(n)$ from the STFT? It would seem so, since we can compute

$$\mathbf{w} \cdot \mathbf{x}(k) = \mathbf{s}(k)$$
$$= \text{IDFT}[\mathbf{S}(k)] \tag{5.10}$$

and use simple division to remove the window. However, this straightforward approach is sensitive to rounding errors, and an overlap-add method produces better results. We will present a simple example here. A similar example is presented in [34].

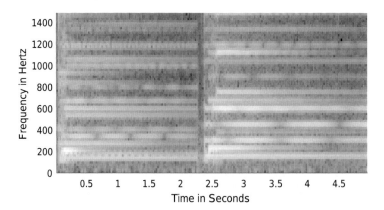

Figure 5.10: Guitar chord progression: STFT.

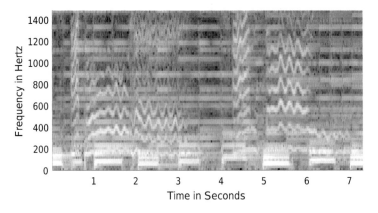

Figure 5.11: Song clip: STFT.

We set $M = L/2$ (50% overlap) and use a Hanning window extended with zeros:

$$w(n) = \begin{cases} 0.5 + 0.5 \cos 2\pi n/L & n = 0, 1, \ldots, L - 1 \\ 0 & \text{otherwise} \end{cases} \tag{5.11}$$

Since we have extended the window function with zeros, we can express the elements of $\mathbf{s}(k)$ as

$$s(k, n) = w(n - kL/2)x(n) \tag{5.12}$$

We now define a signal $y(n)$ as

$$y(n) = \sum_{k=0}^{K-1} s(k, n)$$

$$= \sum_{k=0}^{K-1} w(n - kL/2)x(n) \tag{5.13}$$

where the range of the summation covers the duration of the signal $x(n)$. If

$$\sum_{k=0}^{K-1} w(n - kL/2) = 1 \tag{5.14}$$

then $y(n) = x(n)$, and we have recovered the signal. The Hanning window satisfies this condition.

5.3 Real-Time Spectral Analysis

Suppose we would like to view the STFT of an audio signal with a duration of several minutes or more. This is impractical with the tools we have introduced so far, since the number of signal samples would far exceed the memory capacity of most computers. However, the STFT adapts quite readily to streaming audio.

For convenience, assume that the STFT block length L is an even number and the step size $M = L/2$. Assume further that the audio signal is available as a stream of blocks of M samples. Changing notation a bit, we denote the kth signal block ($k \geq 0$) as

$$\mathbf{x}(k) = \begin{bmatrix} x(kM) & x(kM + 1) & \cdots & x((k+1)M - 1) \end{bmatrix} \tag{5.15}$$

so that the kth STFT block is

$$\mathbf{v}(k) = \begin{bmatrix} \mathbf{x}(k-1) & \mathbf{x}(k) \end{bmatrix} \tag{5.16}$$

where $\mathbf{x}(-1)$ is all zeros. If we again let $\mathbf{s}(k)$ be the windowed version of the STFT block (see Equation (5.7)), then the DFT of $\mathbf{s}(k)$ is the STFT for time period k. Thus, to compute and display the STFT of an arbitrarily long signal, we need no more than two signal blocks at any time.

The MATLAB DSP System Toolbox provides several object-oriented tools for generating and processing streaming data. These tools include data sources (e.g., audio recorder and audio-file reader), signal-processing algorithms, data displays (time and frequency domain), and data sinks (e.g., audio player). A typical script consists of an initialization section to create the required objects and perform any onetime calculations, a signal-processing loop to process the signal data block by block, and a clean-up section. The signal-processing loop can use any combination of provided tools and custom programming.

For example, the following statement creates an audio-file reader object:

```
AFR=dsp.AudioFileReader(filename ,...
    'SamplesPerFrame',blocksize);
```

where **filename** is the name of an audio file and **blocksize** is the number of audio samples in each block of data. Like most streaming objects, the audio-file reader has a **step** method. The statement

```
x=step(AFR);
```

loads the next block of samples into the vector **x**. The **step** method is normally applied within the signal-processing loop. The audio-file reader object also delivers the sampling rate as **AFR.SampleRate**.

The following script, which simply reads and plays an audio file, illustrates some of what we have discussed so far:

```
blocksize=2048
AFR=dsp.AudioFileReader('My_Favorite_Song.wav');
AFR.SamplesPerFrame=blocksize;
AP=dsp.AudioPlayer;
while ~isdone(AFR)
    x=step(AFR);
    step(AP,x);
end
release(AP);
```

The audio-player object has a **step** method that passes the audio to the host computer's sound system. Each iteration of the signal-processing loop gets a block of samples from the audio file and passes it to the audio player. The **isdone** method of the audio-file reader returns **true** when there are no more samples to obtain.

The DSP System Toolbox also contains a spectrum analyzer that, among other things, can produce a plot of the STFT in real time using procedure similar to the one described at the beginning of this section. We need only expand our script to create and run a spectrum analyzer object.

```
blocksize=2048
AFR=dsp.AudioFileReader('My_Favorite_Song.wav');
AFR.SamplesPerFrame=blocksize;
SA=dsp.SpectrumAnalyzer;
SA.SampleRate=AFR.SampleRate;
SA.SpectrumType='Spectrogram';
AP=dsp.AudioPlayer;
while ~isdone(AFR)
    x=step(AFR);
    step(SA,x);
    step(AP,x);
end
```

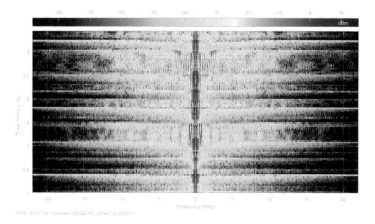

Figure 5.12: Snapshot of real-time STFT display.

```
release(AP);
```

This script produces a real-time display of the STFT of the recorded audio along with real-time audio output. Figure 5.12 is a snapshot of the display. This illustration uses mostly default settings of the spectrum analyzer – there are many options to modify the display.

We will make further use of MATLAB streaming audio in subsequent chapters.

5.4   Spectrum of Resampled Signals

We will conclude this chapter by examining the spectra of the down- and upsampled signals introduced in Chapter 3.

Let $X(k)$ be the DFT of $x(n)$ and express $x(n)$ in terms of the inverse DFT.

$$x(n) = \frac{1}{N} \sum_{k=0}^{N-1} X(k) e^{j2\pi nk/N} \tag{5.17}$$

If we assume $N = KL$ (K and L are both integers), we can rewrite Equation (5.17) as

$$
\begin{aligned}
x(n) &= \frac{1}{N} \sum_{k=0}^{N-1} X(k) e^{j2\pi nk/N} \\
&= \frac{1}{N} \sum_{k=0}^{K-1} \sum_{l=0}^{L-1} X(k+lK) e^{j2\pi n(k+lK)/N} \\
&= \frac{1}{N} \sum_{k=0}^{K-1} e^{j2\pi nk/N} \sum_{l=0}^{L-1} X(k+lK) e^{j2\pi nlK/N}
\end{aligned}
\tag{5.18}
$$

Now, if we downsample $x(n)$ by L we have

$$x(nL) = \frac{1}{N} \sum_{k=0}^{K-1} e^{j2\pi nLk/N} \sum_{l=0}^{L-1} X(k+lK)e^{j2\pi nLlK/N}$$

$$= \frac{1}{N} \sum_{k=0}^{K-1} e^{j2\pi nk/K} \sum_{l=0}^{L-1} X(k+lK)e^{j2\pi nl}$$

$$= \frac{1}{M} \sum_{k=0}^{K-1} e^{j2\pi nk/K} \frac{1}{L} \sum_{l=0}^{L-1} X(k+lK) \qquad (5.19)$$

Thus, the DFT of the downsampled signal is

$$X_D(k) = \frac{1}{L} \sum_{l=0}^{L-1} X(k+lK) \qquad (5.20)$$

Equation (5.20) is sometimes called an *alias function* and indicates how downsampling can introduce aliases, as described in Chapter 3. Thus, it is prudent to apply a low-pass filter prior to downsampling a signal.

If we upsample by L, we obtain a contrasting result. The DFT of the upsampled signal is given by

$$X_U(k) = \sum_{n=0}^{NL-1} x_U(n)e^{-j2\pi kn/NL}$$

$$= \sum_{n=0}^{N-1} x(n)e^{-j2\pi knL/NL}$$

$$= \sum_{n=0}^{N-1} x(n)e^{-j2\pi kn/N} = X(k) \qquad (5.21)$$

At first glance it appears that the DFT is unchanged, but note that the frequency index k now ranges from 0 to $NL - 1$ and recall that $X(k)$ is periodic with period N. Thus, upsampling by L results in L repetitions of the original DFT.

Finally, let us consider the z-transforms of $x_D(n)$ and $x_U(n)$. The upsampling case is straightforward.

$$X_U(z) = \sum_{n=-\infty}^{\infty} x_U(n)z^{-n}$$

$$= \sum_{n=-\infty}^{\infty} x(n)z^{-nL}$$

$$= X(z^L) \qquad (5.22)$$

The downsampling case is trickier. We start in a similar manner.

$$X_D(z) = \sum_{n=-\infty}^{\infty} x_D(n)z^{-n}$$

$$= \sum_{n=-\infty}^{\infty} x(nL)z^{-n} \qquad (5.23)$$

However, we cannot make a simple substitution as in the upsampling case. Instead we use a decimation function $D_L(n)$ to select every L^{th} sample of $x(n)$, i.e.,

$$D_L(n) = \begin{cases} 1 & n \bmod L = 0 \\ 0 & n \bmod L \neq 0 \end{cases} \tag{5.24}$$

Now we can express $X_D(z)$ in terms of all of the signal samples.

$$X_D(z) = \sum_{n=-\infty}^{\infty} D_L(n)x(n)z^{-n/L} \tag{5.25}$$

Next we select a particular version of $D_L(n)$.

$$D_L(n) = \frac{1}{L}\sum_{l=0}^{L-1} e^{j2\pi ln/L} \tag{5.26}$$

Substituting Equation (5.26) into Equation (5.25) produces the final result.

$$\begin{aligned} X_D(z) &= \sum_{n=-\infty}^{\infty} \frac{1}{L}\sum_{l=0}^{L-1} e^{j2\pi ln/L} x(n)z^{-n/L} \\ &= \frac{1}{L}\sum_{l=0}^{L-1}\sum_{n=-\infty}^{\infty} x(n)\left(e^{-j2\pi l/L}z^{1/L}\right)^{-n} \\ &= \frac{1}{L}\sum_{l=0}^{L-1} X\left(e^{-j2\pi l/L}z^{1/L}\right) \end{aligned} \tag{5.27}$$

5.5 Summary

In this chapter we have applied tools based on the DFT to perform frequency domain analysis of real audio signals. We have seen how frequency domain analysis can expose important properties of an audio signal. In the next chapter we will develop additional tools that can modify these properties.

MATLAB Projects

1. Obtain an audio file of a single note played on an instrument with a duration of a few seconds. Write a MATLAB script to:

   - Read the audio file into a vector and obtain the sampling rate.
   - Display a time domain plot of the amplitude of the signal vs. time in seconds.
   - Display a frequency domain plot of the magnitude of the signal vs. frequency in hertz.

   Use the MATLAB function **findpeaks** to determine the magnitudes and frequencies of the most prominent components of the spectrum.

Chapter 6

Frequency-Shaping Filters

It is sometimes desirable to modify the frequency-related characteristics of an audio signal. This modification may be necessary to compensate for distortion or to achieve some desired change in the audio. We use the phrase *frequency-shaping filter* to indicate a mechanism that applies a frequency-dependent gain (or attenuation) to an audio signal. Such a mechanism can be used to emphasize or de-emphasize specified frequency ranges. In this chapter we will present several types of frequency-shaping filters that can be realized as digital LTIS.

Recall that a digital LTIS is completely characterized by a transfer function $H(z)$, which is the bilateral z-transform of the impulse response $h(n)$. If the input to the LTIS is an everlasting sinusoid $x(n) = e^{j\Omega n}$, then the output is $y(n) = H(e^{j\Omega})e^{j\Omega n}$, i.e., an everlasting sinusoid with the same frequency Ω and complex amplitude $H'(\Omega) = H(e^{j\Omega})$, which is the DTFT of $h(n)$. This complex amplitude, which we will denote further as just $H(\Omega)$, describes the *frequency response* of the LTIS. Our goal, therefore, is to design digital LTIS such that $H(\Omega)$ provides the desired frequency-shaping.

Digital filter design is a very well established topic that is thoroughly covered in many texts (e.g., [8]). We will limit our attention here to a few basic filter types and design methods.

6.1 A Simple Filter

Consider a digital LTIS characterized by the following difference equation:

$$y(n) = \alpha y(n-1) + (1-\alpha)x(n) \tag{6.1}$$

The transfer function can readily be obtained by taking the z-transform of Equation (6.1).

$$Y(z) = \alpha z^{-1}Y(z) + (1-\alpha)X(z) \tag{6.2}$$

The transfer function is given by

$$H(z) = \frac{Y(z)}{X(z)} = \frac{1-\alpha}{1-\alpha z^{-1}} \tag{6.3}$$

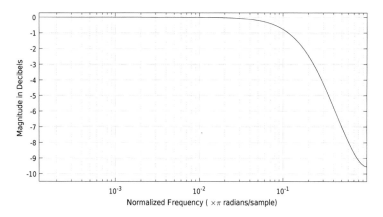

Figure 6.1: Frequency response of a simple filter ($\alpha = 0.5$).

The frequency response of this system is obtained by setting $z = e^{j\Omega}$ and plotting the magnitude and phase of the transfer function vs. Ω. We have previously seen how we can use the MATLAB function `freqz` to calculate and plot the frequency response. We can also use `fvtool`, the MATLAB filter visualization tool. `fvtool` can be used in a number of ways, but the simplest in this case is to provide it with the numerator (**b**) and denominator (**a**) of the transfer function. The following MATLAB script provides the desired result:

```
alpha=0.5;
b=1-alpha;
a=[1 -alpha];
h=fvtool(b,a);
set(h,'FrequencyScale','Log')
```

Figure 6.1 shows the magnitude of the frequency response for $\alpha = 0.5$.

Our simple filter is an example of a *low-pass* filter, in that the magnitude of the frequency response is 0 dB for frequencies from 0 radians/sample up to a certain frequency (about $\pi/10$ radians per sample in this case) but drops rapidly for higher frequencies. The low-pass filter is an example of a frequency-shaping filter that can modify the frequency spectrum of a signal to obtain some desired result. The low-pass filter and some other types of filters can be defined in terms of a *pass band* and a *stop band* with related frequencies and gains. For a low-pass filter, the pass band includes frequencies from 0 radians/sample up to the pass-band frequency Ω_p and the stop band includes frequencies from the stop-band frequency Ω_s up to the Nyquist frequency π ($\Omega_s > \Omega_p$). The gain, which is the magnitude of the transfer function, is approximately unity (0 dB) in the pass band and lower in the stop band. In addition to the low-pass filter, we can define the following filter types in terms of pass and stop bands:

- high-pass filter: The opposite of low-pass. The stop band ranges from 0 to Ω_s radians/sample, and the pass band ranges from Ω_p to π radians/sample ($\Omega_p > \Omega_s$).

- band-pass filter: The pass band ranges from some lower frequency Ω_1 to some upper frequency Ω_2.

- band-stop filter: The opposite of band-pass. The stop band ranges from some lower frequency Ω_1 to some upper frequency Ω_2. The band-stop filter is sometimes called a *notch* filter.

In the case of a band-pass filter, the lower stop band ends at some frequency $\Omega_{s1} < \Omega_1$ and the upper stop band begins at some frequency $\Omega_{s2} > \Omega_2$. A similar statement applies to the band-stop filter. Thus, in every case, the pass band(s) and stop band(s) are separated by gaps. Ideally the gaps would be 0, but reality imposes finite gaps.

Note that although we use the word "gain" to characterize a filter, the value of the gain is often less than unity (less than 0 dB). This is definitely true for a passive filter. Nevertheless, we will often refer to the magnitude of the filter transfer function as the filter's gain.

Another type of filter that is very useful for audio signal processing is the *peak filter*, which has a gain of unity (0 dB) except for a range of frequencies in which the gain is higher (boost) or lower (cut). If the range starts at 0 radians/sample, we may call the filter a *bass shelf filter*, and if the range ends at π radians/sample, we may call the filter a *treble shelf filter*.

The simple filter presented earlier is an example of a *recursive* filter, in that its output $y(n)$ depends on previous outputs (in this case the most recent output $y(n-1)$) as well as the current input (and, in general, previous inputs). The impulse response of a recursive filter continues indefinitely, and therefore recursive filters are also called *infinite impulse response* (IIR) filters. The transfer function $H(z)$ of a recursive filter has the following general form:

$$H(z) = \frac{b_0 + b_1 z^{-1} + b_2 z^{-2} + \cdots + b_N z^{-N}}{a_0 + a_1 z^{-1} + a_2 z^{-2} + \cdots + a_N z^{-N}} \tag{6.4}$$

Without loss of generality we can set $a_0 = 1$, and this is often the convention. The integer N is called the *order* of the filter. Thus, our simple low-pass filter is a first-order filter.

Note that if $a_0 = 1$ and $a_n = 0$ for $n > 0$, then $H(z)$ is the z-transform of an impulse response given by

$$h(n) = \begin{cases} b_n & 0 \leq n \leq N \\ 0 & n > N \end{cases} \tag{6.5}$$

Thus, the corresponding impulse response has a finite number of terms. Such a filter is called a *finite impulse response* (FIR) filter. We will mostly consider IIR filters in this book.

The output of a filter is determined by the corresponding difference equation, i.e.,

$$y(n) = -\sum_{m=1}^{N} a_m y(n - m) + \sum_{m=0}^{N} b_m x(n - m) \tag{6.6}$$

In MATLAB this becomes

```
y=filter(b,a,x);
```

where x is a vector of the input samples and b and a are vectors of the b_n and a_n coefficients, respectively.

So it all comes down to determining the values of the b_n and a_n coefficients that provide the desired frequency response. Let us now see how this might be done.

6.2 Second-Order Filters

In this section we will use second-order filters as a means to illustrate the basic approach to recursive filter design and to develop some very useful filter types.

A second-order filter is simply one whose transfer function is given by Equation (6.4) with $N = 2$, i.e.,

$$H(z) = \frac{b_0 + b_1 z^{-1} + b_2 z^{-2}}{1 + a_1 z^{-1} + a_2 z^{-2}} \tag{6.7}$$

We can determine $H(z)$ by a two-step process:

1. Determine a suitable analog transfer function $H_a(s)$.

2. Convert $H_a(s)$ to an equivalent $H(z)$.

The latter step can be accomplished using the *bilinear transform* given by

$$s = 2f_s \frac{z-1}{z+1} \tag{6.8}$$

where f_s is the sampling rate. Stated another way, $H(z)$ is given by

$$H(z) = H_a(s)|_{s=2f_s \frac{z-1}{z+1}} \tag{6.9}$$

Or we can use a variation of this transform, which forces $H(z)$ to match $H_a(s)$ exactly at a specified frequency f_p.

$$s = \frac{2\pi f_p}{\tan(\pi f_p/f_s)} \frac{z-1}{z+1} \tag{6.10}$$

Both of these options are supported by the MATLAB function `bilinear`, which we will use in examples that follow.

6.2.1 Second-Order Peak Filter

Consider the analog transfer function given by

$$H_a(s) = \frac{s^2 + g\omega_0 s/Q + \omega_0^2}{s^2 + \omega_0 s/Q + \omega_0^2} \tag{6.11}$$

The corresponding frequency response is given by $H_a(j\omega)$ (ω is the frequency in radians/second) and a few points on the frequency response are evident by inspection:

$$H_a(j0) = 1$$
$$H_a(j\omega_0) = g$$
$$\lim_{\omega \to \infty} H_a(j\omega) = 1$$

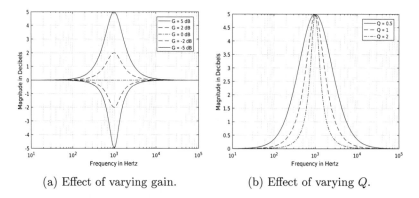

(a) Effect of varying gain.   (b) Effect of varying Q.

Figure 6.2: Frequency response of an analog peak filter.

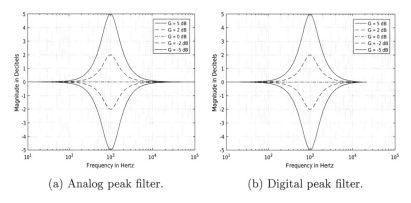

(a) Analog peak filter.   (b) Digital peak filter.

Figure 6.3: Peak filter frequency response.

It is also true that the frequency response reaches a maximum or a minimum at $\omega = \omega_0$. Figure 6.2a shows the frequency response for $f_0 = 1000$ Hz, $Q = 1$, and various values of peak gain (in decibels). Figure 6.2b shows the effect of varying Q. Thus, we can use the peak filter to boost ($g > 1$) or cut ($g < 1$) a signal at a given frequency, and the frequency range affected by the boost/cut can be varied by varying Q.

Note the lack of symmetry in Figure 6.2a, i.e., the cuts are narrower than the corresponding boosts. This can be remedied by using a slightly different transfer function for $g < 1$:

$$H_a(s) = \frac{s^2 + \omega_0 s/Q + \omega_0^2}{s^2 + \omega_0 s/gQ + \omega_0^2} \tag{6.12}$$

This results in the improved response shown in Figure 6.3a.

Now that we have a suitable analog filter design, we need only to apply the bilinear transform to convert it to its digital counterpart. This can be done manually using the bilinear transform given by Equation (6.8) or, with much less effort and less chance of error, using the MATLAB function `bilinear`. For a peak filter with $g > 1$ the key elements of a MATLAB script are simply:

```
g=10^{G/20};
w0=2*pi*f0;
B=[1 g*w0/Q w0^2];
A=[1 w0/Q w0^2];
[b,a]=bilinear(B,A,fs,f0);
```

where G is the gain in decibels, f0 is the peak frequency f_0 in hertz, Q is Q, and fs is the sampling rate f_s. Figure 6.3b shows the frequency response of the resulting digital filter (both boosted and cut). Note the close resemblance to Figure 6.3a.

Although the MATLAB function fvtool is the most straightforward way to display frequency response, the function freqz may offer more flexibility. The basic approach used to create Figure 6.3b is:

```
f=logspace(1,log10(fs/2),200);
h=freqz(b,a,f,fs);
semilogx(f,20*log10(abs(h)))
```

Figure 6.4 shows pole-zero plots for peak filters with $f_0 = 4000$ Hz and two values of gain. Note that there are two poles and two zeros and that the complex poles and zeros are in conjugate pairs.

6.2.2 Shelf Filters

Bass and treble shelf filters can be designed in the same manner as the peak filter. A suitable analog transfer function for a bass shelf filter is given by

$$H_a(s) = \begin{cases} \dfrac{s^2 + \sqrt{2g}\omega_b s + g\omega_b^2}{s^2 + \sqrt{2}\omega_b s + \omega_b^2} & g > 1 \\[3mm] \dfrac{s^2 + \sqrt{2}\omega_b s + \omega_b^2}{s^2 + \sqrt{2/g}\omega_b s + \omega_b^2/g} & g < 1 \end{cases} \tag{6.13}$$

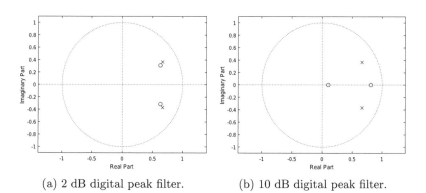

(a) 2 dB digital peak filter.　　　　(b) 10 dB digital peak filter.

Figure 6.4: Peak filter pole-zero plots.

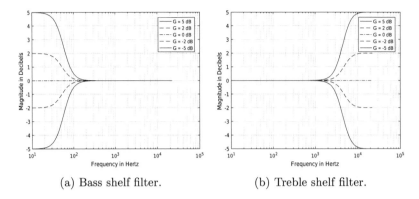

(a) Bass shelf filter.   (b) Treble shelf filter.

Figure 6.5: Frequency response of a digital shelf filter.

and one for a treble shelf filter is given by

$$H_a(s) = \begin{cases} \dfrac{gs^2 + \sqrt{2g}\omega_t s + \omega_t^2}{s^2 + \sqrt{2}\omega_t s + \omega_t^2} & g > 1 \\[3mm] \dfrac{s^2 + \sqrt{2}\omega_t s + \omega_t^2}{s^2/g + \sqrt{2/g}\omega_t s + \omega_t^2} & g < 1 \end{cases} \tag{6.14}$$

where ω_b and ω_t are the bass and treble transition frequencies, respectively. Frequency responses for bass and treble shelf filters are shown in Figure 6.5a and 6.5b.

6.2.3 MATLAB Implementation

The following MATLAB function determines the coefficients of a second-order shelf or peak filter based on the gain in decibels, the peak or transition frequency in hertz, the Q factor (peak filter only), and the sampling rate f_s:

```
function [b,a]=order2Filt(G,f0,Q,fs,type)
g=10^(G/20);
w0=2*pi*f0;
if (strcmp(type,'Bass')==1)
    if (g>1)
        B=[1 sqrt(2*g)*w0 g*w0^2];
        A=[1 sqrt(2)*w0 w0^2];
    else
        B=[1 sqrt(2)*w0 w0^2];
        A=[1 sqrt(2/g)*w0 (w0^2)/g];
    end
elseif (strcmp(type,'Treble')==1)
    if (g>1)
        B=[g sqrt(2*g)*w0 w0^2];
        A=[1 sqrt(2)*w0 w0^2];
    else
        B=[1 sqrt(2)*w0 w0^2];
        A=[1/g sqrt(2/g)*w0 w0^2];
```

```
        end
elseif (strcmp(type, 'Peak')==1)
    if (g>1)
        B=[1 g*w0/Q w0^2];
        A=[1 w0/Q w0^2];
    else
        B=[1 w0/Q w0^2];
        A=[1 w0/(g*Q) w0^2];
    end
else
    error(['Unsupported_Filter_Type:_' type]);
end
[b,a]=bilinear(B,A,fs,f0);
```

6.2.4 Audio Equalizer

Peak and shelf filters can be cascaded to create a multichannel audio equalizer. The overall transfer function of the equalizer is given by

$$H_{\mathrm{EQ}}(z) = H_{\mathrm{B}}(z)H_1(z)\dots H_N(z)H_{\mathrm{T}}(z) \tag{6.15}$$

where $H_{\mathrm{B}}(z)$ is the bass shelf transfer function, $H_1(z)\dots H_N(z)$ are the peak filter transfer functions, and $H_{\mathrm{T}}(z)$ is the treble shelf transfer function. Each of these transfer functions has the form of Equation (6.7) and is sometimes referred to as a *biquadratic* function or as a *second-order section*. A cascade of second-order sections can be completely specified by an $N \times 6$ matrix of filter coefficients given by

$$\mathbf{S} = \begin{bmatrix} b_{01} & b_{11} & b_{21} & 1 & a_{11} & a_{21} \\ \vdots & \vdots & \vdots & \vdots & \vdots & \vdots \\ b_{0N} & b_{1N} & b_{2N} & 1 & a_{1N} & a_{2N} \end{bmatrix} \tag{6.16}$$

The nth row of the matrix contains the coefficients of the nth section of the filter. The MATLAB function **fvtool** can be called using this matrix, which is referred to as the SOS matrix, instead of the **b** and **a** vectors. The MATLAB function **sosfilt** replaces **filter** using the SOS matrix. Figure 6.6 is a plot of the frequency response of a 6-band equalizer consisting of the cascade of a bass shelf filter, four peak filters, and a treble shelf filter, all designed as described earlier. The critical frequencies of the sections are distributed logarithmically from 20 Hz to 8000 Hz. All of the gains are set to 0 dB, except for the bass shelf filter and one of the peak filters.

6.3 Low-Pass Filter Design

Besides the fact that the low-pass filter is very useful in audio signal processing, it can also serve as the basis for a high-pass, band-pass, or band-stop filter. Thus, we will examine the low-pass filter in more detail. There are a number of classic designs for the low-pass filter, and detailed presentations of these designs can be found in the literature [8]. Instead of duplicating these presentations, we will make use of the MATLAB implementations of these designs and present examples.

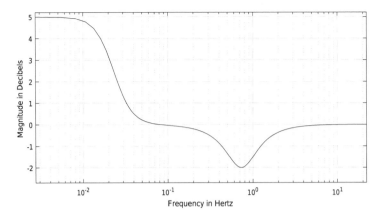

Figure 6.6: Frequency response of 6-band equalizer.

Like the second-order filters, these filter designs are derived from corresponding analog filter designs using the bilinear transform.

6.3.1   Low-Pass Filter Specification

We can specify a low-pass filter in terms of desired characteristics of the pass band and stop band:

- pass-band frequency f_{pb} – The upper limit of the range of pass-band frequencies. Recall that the pass band for a low-pass filter begins at 0 Hz.

- stop-band frequency f_{sb} – The lower limit of the range of stop-band frequencies. Recall that the stop band for a low-pass filter ends at the Nyquist frequency $f_s/2$ Hz.

- pass-band ripple R_p – The maximum deviation from 0 dB of the filter gain within the pass band.

- stop-band attenuation A_s – The minimum attenuation (in decibels) within the stop band. Thus, the stop-band gain should be less than $-A_s$ dB.

Although there is no constraint on the gain in the gap between f_{pb} and f_{sb}, the gain generally decreases monotonically in this frequency range.

6.3.2   Butterworth Low-Pass Filter

The Butterworth filter is specified by two parameters: the order N (a positive integer > 1) and a normalized cutoff frequency W_c ($0 \leq W_c \leq 1$). Note that the normalized frequency W is simply the frequency in radians/sample Ω divided by π. Figure 6.7 is a plot of the magnitude of the frequency response (expressed as a factor rather than decibels) for four Butterworth filters with normalized cutoff frequency $W_c = 0.2$ ($\Omega_c = 0.2\pi$ radians/sample) and order $N = 2, 4, 8, 16$.

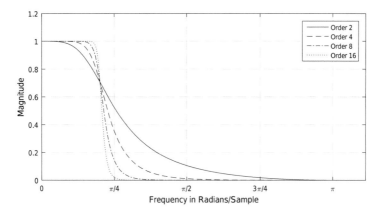

Figure 6.7: Frequency response of Butterworth low-pass filters.

Note the following characteristics of the Butterworth LPF:

- The magnitude of the frequency response decreases monotonically with frequency.

- Although there is deviation from 0 dB in the pass band, it does not display itself as ripple, but we use the term nonetheless.

- Regardless of the order, the magnitude of the frequency response is $1/\sqrt{2}$ at the cutoff frequency.

- As the order increases the frequency response approaches that of an ideal low-pass filter.

The MATLAB function **butter** determines the filter coefficients b_n and a_n based on the filter order N (first argument) and the normalized cutoff frequency W_c (second argument):

```
[b,a]=butter(N,Wc);
```

The coefficients are returned as $1 \times (N+1)$ arrays **b** and **a**.

Examining Figure 6.7, we see that increasing the order of the filter allows us to either reduce the gap between the end of the pass band and the beginning of the stop band, decrease the pass-band ripple, increase the stop-band attenuation, or a combination of these. On the other hand, we might want to know the lowest-order (and thus simplest and fastest) filter that can meet our specification. The MATLAB function **buttord** determines the order and the normalized cutoff frequency of the lowest-order Butterworth filter that meets the specification. The output of **buttord** becomes the input to **butter**. This is done in the following MATLAB script:

```
fpb=1000;  fsb=2000;  fs=44100;
Rp=2;  As=50;
[N,Oc]=buttord(2*fpb/fs,2*fsb/fs,Rp,As);
[b,a]=butter(N,Oc);
h=fvtool(b,a);
h.Fs=fs;
h.FrequencyScale='Log';
```

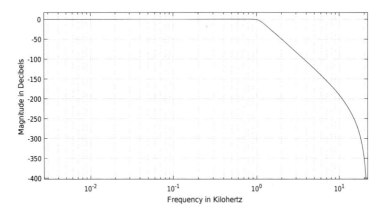

Figure 6.8: Frequency response of specified Butterworth filter.

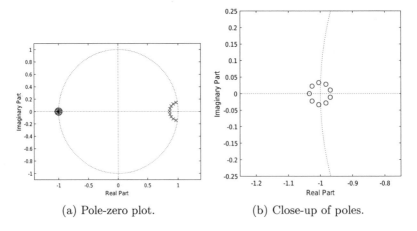

(a) Pole-zero plot.   (b) Close-up of poles.

Figure 6.9: Butterworth filter pole-zero plot.

This example includes normalization of the pass-band and stop-band frequencies using the sampling frequency f_s. It also includes some adjustments to fvtool to display frequency in hertz on a logarithmic scale. In this example buttord yields a filter of order 9 with a normalized cutoff frequency of 0.048π radians/sample (1060 Hz). Figure 6.8 shows the filter frequency response. Note that the magnitude of the frequency response at 2 kHz is -50 dB, as specified. Figure 6.9 shows the poles and zeros of this Butterworth filter. Note that there are 9 poles and 9 zeros, matching the order of the filter.

Low-pass filters have many applications in audio signal processing. Figure 6.10 illustrates an example: recovering a signal that has been corrupted by noise. The upper plot shows the original signal, which is a summation of three sinusoidal signals simulating a major triad. The middle plot shows the result of adding white Gaussian noise, which approximates noise found in real systems, to the signal. The lower plot shows the result of passing the corrupted signal through a Butterworth low-pass filter. The figure shows that the filter removes most of the noise without significantly distorting the original signal.

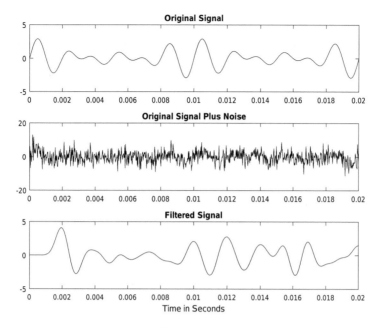

Figure 6.10: Example: filtering signal corrupted by noise.

Figure 6.10 was generated by the following MATLAB script:

```
fs =44100;
T=0.02;
N=round(fs*T);
t=linspace(0,T,N);
f0 =100;
x=sin(2*pi*4*f0*t)+sin(2*pi*5*f0*t)+sin(2*pi*6*f0*t);
subplot(3,1,1); plot(t,x);
title('Original_Signal');
n=wgn(1,N,10);
subplot(3,1,2); plot(t,x+n);
title('Original_Signal_Plus_Noise');
fpb=8*f0;
fsb =1.75*fpb;
Rpb=1;
Asb=50;
[Nb,Oc]=buttord(2*fpb/fs,2*fsb/fs,Rpb,Asb);
[b,a]=butter(Nb,Oc);
y=filter(b,a,x+n);
subplot(3,1,3); plot(t,y);
title('Filtered_Signal');
xlabel('Time_in_Seconds');
```

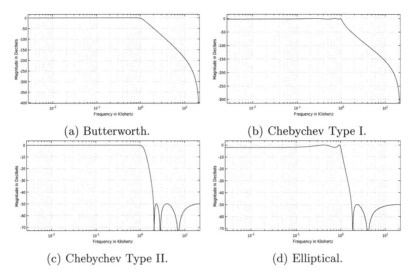

(a) Butterworth.   (b) Chebychev Type I.

(c) Chebychev Type II.   (d) Elliptical.

Figure 6.11: Four low-pass filters designed to the same specification.

6.3.3   Other Low-Pass Filters

As mentioned earlier, there are other classic approaches to filter design, including two types of Chebychev filters and the elliptical filter. MATLAB functions similar to `buttord` and `butter` are available for these three designs. Figure 6.11 shows the frequency response of the four filter types, all designed to the same specification ($f_{pb} = 1000$ Hz, $f_{sb} = 2000$ Hz, $R_p = 2$ dB, $A_s = 50$ dB and $f_s = 44\,100$ Hz). Some observations:

- The Chebychev type I filter exhibits ripple in the pass band but not in the stop band.

- The Chebychev type II filter exhibits ripple in the stop band but not in the pass band.

- The elliptical filter exhibits ripple in both the pass band and the stop band.

Further analysis of the four filters reveals that the order of the Butterworth filter is 9, the order of the two Chebychev filters is 6, and the order of the elliptical filter is 4. The cost of implementing the filter (e.g., CPU time and memory) generally increases with the order.

So when it comes to designing low-pass filters, we enjoy an embarrassment of riches thanks to the Butterworths, Chebychevs, and others who have gone before us.

6.4   High-Pass, Band-Pass, and Band-Stop Filters

As mentioned earlier, the low-pass filter can serve as a basis for other filters in its family. We will illustrate this with a second-order Butterworth filter.

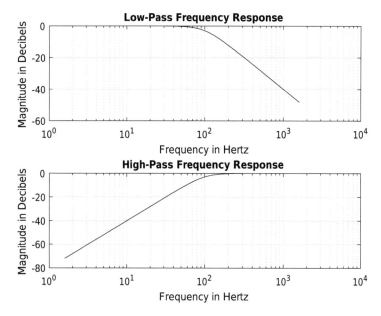

Figure 6.12: Low-pass and high-pass frequency response.

The transfer function of a normalized, second-order analog Butterworth low-pass filter is given by

$$H_a(s) = \frac{1}{s^2 + \sqrt{2}s + 1} \tag{6.17}$$

This filter has a cutoff frequency of 1 radian/second. To change the cutoff frequency to a desired value $\omega_c = 2\pi f_c$, we simply replace s with s/ω_c, which yields

$$H_L(s) = \frac{\omega_c^2}{s^2 + \sqrt{2}\omega_c s + \omega_c^2} \tag{6.18}$$

To obtain a high-pass filter with cutoff frequency ω_c, we replace s in the normalized transfer function with ω_c/s, which yields

$$H_H(s) = \frac{s^2}{s^2 + \sqrt{2}\omega_c s + \omega_c^2} \tag{6.19}$$

Figure 6.12 shows plots of the frequency responses corresponding to $H_L(s)$ and $H_H(s)$ for $f_c = 100$ Hz.

Similar adjustments to the normalized transfer function lead to band-pass and band-stop filters. For $\omega_2 > \omega_1$

$$s \Rightarrow \frac{s^2 + \omega_1\omega_2}{(\omega_2 - \omega_1)s} \tag{6.20}$$

converts the normalized low-pass filter to a band-pass filter and

$$s \Rightarrow \frac{(\omega_2 - \omega_1)s}{s^2 + \omega_1\omega_2} \tag{6.21}$$

N_x	Number of state variables
N_u	Number of input channels
N_y	Number of output channels
x	State vector
u	Input vector
y	Output vector
A	$N_x \times N_x$ matrix
B	$N_x \times N_u$ matrix
C	$N_y \times N_x$ matrix
D	$N_x \times N_u$ matrix

Table 6.1: State-space model parameters.

converts the normalized low-pass filter to a band-stop filter. These substitutions are rather tedious even for a second-order filter, but fortunately the MATLAB filter functions (`butter` etc.) take care of the details.

6.5   State-Space Filters

The *state-space* model is a useful alternate representation of a dynamic system. State space models are popular for the analysis of communication systems and control systems. MATLAB supports state-space models and provides useful functions for designing and analyzing them.

The state-space model of a digital LTIS is as follows:

$$\mathbf{x}(n+1) = \mathbf{A}\mathbf{x}(n) + \mathbf{B}\mathbf{u}(n)$$
$$\mathbf{y}(n) = \mathbf{C}\mathbf{x}(n) + \mathbf{D}\mathbf{u}(n) \tag{6.22}$$

The parameters in Equation (6.22) are defined in Table 6.1. In the case of a time-invariant system, the matrices **A**, **B**, **C**, and **D** are constants. The matrix **A** is sometimes called the *state transition matrix*.

The state-space model is centered around the *state vector* $\mathbf{x}(n)$. Given the initial value of the state vector $\mathbf{x}(0)$ and the values of the input $\mathbf{u}(n)$ for $n \geq 0$, we can determine both the state vector and the output $\mathbf{y}(n)$ for $n \geq 0$. The general formula for $\mathbf{x}(n)$ is

$$\mathbf{x}(n) = \mathbf{A}^n\mathbf{x}(0) + \sum_{k=0}^{n-1} \mathbf{A}^{n-1-k}\mathbf{B}\mathbf{u}(k) \tag{6.23}$$

Note that the second term in Equation (6.23) is a convolution sum.

We can also solve Equation (6.22) using the z-transform. Applying the z-transform to Equation (6.22) we have

$$z\mathbf{X}(z) = \mathbf{A}\mathbf{X}(z) + \mathbf{B}\mathbf{U}(z) \tag{6.24}$$

so that

$$\mathbf{X}(z) = (z\mathbf{I} - \mathbf{A})^{-1}\mathbf{B}\mathbf{U}(z) \tag{6.25}$$

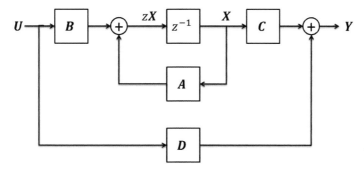

Figure 6.13: Block diagram of general state-space filter.

Thus, the output is given by

$$\mathbf{Y}(z) = \left[\mathbf{C}(z\mathbf{I} - \mathbf{A})^{-1}\mathbf{B} + \mathbf{D}\right]\mathbf{U}(z)$$
$$= \mathbf{H}(z)\mathbf{U}(z) \tag{6.26}$$

where

$$\mathbf{H}(z) = \mathbf{C}(z\mathbf{I} - \mathbf{A})^{-1}\mathbf{B} + \mathbf{D} \tag{6.27}$$

The matrix $\mathbf{H}(z)$ is a matrix of transfer functions relating the outputs to the inputs.

Figure 6.13 is a block diagram of a general state-space filter in z-transform notation.

6.5.1 State-Space Model of a Recursive Filter

Equation (6.4) is the transfer function of a general recursive filter of order N with a single input and output. The corresponding state-space filter is given by

$$\mathbf{A} = \begin{bmatrix} 0 & 1 & 0 & \cdots & 0 & 0 \\ 0 & 0 & 1 & \cdots & 0 & 0 \\ \vdots & \vdots & \vdots & \ddots & \vdots & \vdots \\ 0 & 0 & 0 & \cdots & 0 & 1 \\ -a_0 & -a_1 & -a_2 & \cdots & -a_{N-2} & -a_{N-1} \end{bmatrix}$$

$$\mathbf{B} = \begin{bmatrix} 0 \\ 0 \\ \vdots \\ 0 \\ 1 \end{bmatrix}$$

$$\mathbf{C} = \begin{bmatrix} b_0 & b_1 & \cdots & b_{N-1} \end{bmatrix}$$
$$\mathbf{D} = 0 \tag{6.28}$$

Note that the number of state variables N_x is equal to N, the order of the filter.

MATLAB provides a pair of functions, `tf2ss` and `ss2tf` to convert between the transfer function model Equation (6.4) and the state-space model:

```
[A,B,C,D]=tf2ss(b,a)
[b,a]=ss2tf(A,B,C,D)
```

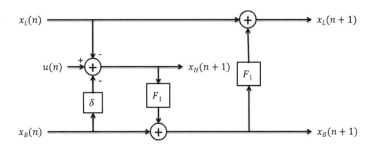

Figure 6.14: Block diagram of example state-space filter.

These functions work for both continuous-time and discrete-time systems.

6.5.2   A Useful State-Space Filter

The following filter tends to pop up in audio applications: [22]

$$x_H(n+1) = -x_L(n) - \delta x_B(n) + u(n)$$
$$x_B(n+1) = F_1 x_H(n+1) + x_B(n)$$
$$x_L(n+1) = F_1 x_B(n+1) + x_L(n) \tag{6.29}$$

where

$$F_1 = 2\sin \pi f_c / f_s \tag{6.30}$$

and δ is a given damping factor. The frequency f_c is either the center or cutoff frequency, and f_s is the sampling rate. This simple, second-order filter provides a high-pass output $x_H(n)$, a band-pass output $x_B(n)$, and a low-pass output $x_L(n)$. Although Equation (6.29) is not in true state-space form, we can transform it readily enough. And Equation (6.29) leads to a simple and efficient calculation if we carry it out in the order listed. Figure 6.14 is a block diagram of the filter.

To transform Equation (6.29) to state-space form, we first identify a state vector $\mathbf{x}(n)$ as

$$\mathbf{x}(n) = \begin{bmatrix} x_H(n) \\ x_B(n) \\ x_L(n) \end{bmatrix} \tag{6.31}$$

Next we substitute the first expression in Equation (6.29) into the second.

$$x_B(n+1) = F_1 \left[-x_L(n) - \delta x_B(n) + u(n) \right] + x_B(n)$$
$$= -F_1 x_L(n) + (1 - \delta F_1)x_B(n) + F_1 u(n) \tag{6.32}$$

Finally, we substitute this expression into the third expression in Equation (6.29).

$$x_L(n+1) = F_1 \left[-F_1 x_L(n) + (1 - \delta F_1)x_B(n) + F_1 u(n) \right] + x_L(n)$$
$$= (1 - F_1^2)x_L(n) + F_1(1 - \delta F_1)x_B(n) + F_1^2 u(n) \tag{6.33}$$

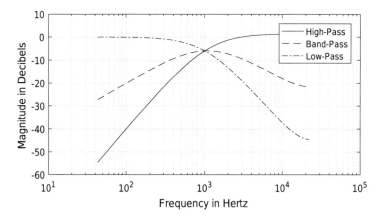

Figure 6.15: Frequency response of example state-space filter.

Now we can write the state equation in matrix form.

$$
\begin{bmatrix} x_H(n+1) \\ x_B(n+1) \\ x_L(n+1) \end{bmatrix} = \begin{bmatrix} 0 & -\delta & -1 \\ 0 & 1-\delta F_1 & -F_1 \\ 0 & F_1(1-\delta F_1) & 1-F_1^2 \end{bmatrix} \begin{bmatrix} x_H(n) \\ x_B(n) \\ x_L(n) \end{bmatrix} + \begin{bmatrix} 1 \\ F_1 \\ F_1^2 \end{bmatrix} u(n) \qquad (6.34)
$$

The outputs $y_H(n)$, $y_B(n)$, and $y_L(n)$ are identical to the state variables, so $\mathbf{C} = \mathbf{I}$, a 3×3 identity matrix

We can use functions from the MATLAB Control Systems Toolbox to determine the frequency response of this filter. First we use the function $\mathtt{ss}$ to create a system object from the matrices $\mathbf{A}$, $\mathbf{B}$, $\mathbf{C}$, and $\mathbf{D}$. Then we use the function $\mathtt{freqresp}$ to calculate the frequency response. The following script produces the example plot shown in Figure 6.15:

```
fc =1000;  fs =44100;  damp=2;
F1=2*sin(pi*fc/fs);
A=[0 −damp −1
    0 1−damp*F1 −F1
    0 F1*(1−damp*F1) 1−F1^2];
B=[1
    F1
    F1^2];
f=linspace(0,fs/2,512);
sys=ss(A,B,eye(3),zeros(3,1),1/fs);
H=freqresp(sys,2*pi*f);
semilogx(f,20*log10(abs(squeeze(H))));
grid on;
xlabel('Frequency_in_Hz');
ylabel('Magnitude_in_dB');
legend('High−Pass','Band−Pass','Low−Pass');
```

The filter seems to be slightly imperfect in that the pass-band gain of the high-pass output is somewhat greater than 0 dB.

In Chapter 7 we will apply this filter to the creation of audio effects.

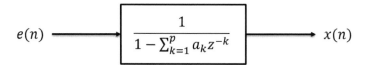

Figure 6.16: Linear predictive coding source model.

6.6   Filters and Source Models

Throughout this book, we have treated the audio signal $x(n)$ as an independent quantity. It is sometimes useful, however, to view $x(n)$ as the output of a system driven by some lower-level excitation. *Linear predictive coding* (LPC) is an example of this approach. Figure 6.16 illustrates an LPC source model in which the audio signal $x(n)$ is the output of an LTIS driven by an excitation signal $e(n)$. The LTIS transfer function, given by

$$H(z) = \frac{1}{1 - \sum_{k=1}^{p} a_k z^{-k}} \tag{6.35}$$

is an example of an *all-pole* filter. The output $x(n)$ is determined by the current input $e(n)$ and the p most recent outputs. Normally our task is to determine $x(n)$ from $e(n)$ and the coefficients $a_1, \ldots, a_k$. To create the LPC source model, however, we must determine $e(n)$ and the LPC coefficients from a given sequence $x(0), x(1), \ldots, x(N-1)$.

From Equation (6.35) we can determine that

$$x(n) = \sum_{k=1}^{p} a_k x(n-k) + e(n) \tag{6.36}$$

To determine $e(n)$ and the LPC coefficients from Equation (6.36) we need to impose some kind of criterion. The LPC source model is based on minimizing the total energy of the excitation signal as given by

$$E = \sum_{n=0}^{N-1} e^2(n)$$

$$= \sum_{n=0}^{N-1} \left[x(n) - \sum_{k=1}^{p} a_k x(n-k) \right]^2 \tag{6.37}$$

Thus, we have for $j = 1, 2, \ldots, p$

$$\frac{\partial E}{\partial a_j} = 0 = \sum_{n=0}^{N-1} 2 \left[x(n) - \sum_{k=1}^{p} a_k x(n-k) \right] x(n-j)$$

$$= 2 \sum_{n=0}^{N-1} x(n)x(n-j) - 2 \sum_{n=0}^{N-1} \sum_{k=1}^{p} a_k x(n-k)x(n-j)$$

$$= 2 \sum_{n=0}^{N-1} x(n)x(n-j) - 2 \sum_{k=1}^{p} \left[\sum_{n=0}^{N-1} x(n-k)x(n-j) \right] a_k \tag{6.38}$$

We can drop the common factor 2 from Equation (6.38). If we extend $x(n)$ by setting $x(n) = 0$ for $n < 0$ and $n \geq N$, then Equation (6.38) becomes

$$\sum_{k=1}^{p} \left[\sum_{n=-\infty}^{\infty} x(n-k)x(n-j) \right] a_k = \sum_{n=-\infty}^{\infty} x(n)x(n-j) \tag{6.39}$$

which can also be written as

$$\sum_{k=1}^{p} \left[\sum_{n=-\infty}^{\infty} x(n)x(n-j+k) \right] a_k = \sum_{n=-\infty}^{\infty} x(n)x(n-j) \tag{6.40}$$

The infinite summation in Equation (6.39) is the well-known autocorrelation function, i.e.,

$$R(m) = \sum_{n=-\infty}^{\infty} x(n)x(n-m) \tag{6.41}$$

so that Equation (6.39) finally becomes

$$\sum_{k=1}^{p} R(j-k)a_k = R(j) \tag{6.42}$$

for $j = 1, 2, \ldots, p$. Equation (6.42) can be written in matrix form as

$$\begin{bmatrix} R(0) & R(1) & \cdots & R(p-1) \\ R(1) & R(0) & \cdots & R(p-2) \\ \vdots & \vdots & \ddots & \vdots \\ R(p-1) & R(p-2) & \cdots & R(0) \end{bmatrix} \begin{bmatrix} a_1 \\ a_2 \\ \vdots \\ a_p \end{bmatrix} = \begin{bmatrix} R(1) \\ R(2) \\ \vdots \\ R(p) \end{bmatrix} \tag{6.43}$$

Thus, the LPC coefficients can be determined by calculating the autocorrelations $R(0)$ through $R(p)$ and solving Equation (6.43). Although Equation (6.43) can be solved by a number of methods, it is usually solved using the Levinson-Durbin algorithm [37], which takes advantage of the form of the matrix of correlations.

Given the LPC coefficients, we can determine the excitation function $e(n)$ from Equation (6.36).

$$e(n) = x(n) - \sum_{k=1}^{p} a_k x(n-k) \tag{6.44}$$

The result is an alternate representation of $x(n)$ based on an excitation function $e(n)$ driving an all-pole filter $H(z)$. But what advantage does this alternate representation provide? Before addressing this, let us consider an example.

Example 6.6.1. Figure 6.17 is a plot of a 200 ms segment of audio. We can determine the LPC coefficients for this signal using the MATLAB function `lpc`:

```
p=6;
a=lpc(x,p);
```

where `p` is the chosen number of poles, `x` is the signal vector and `a` is the length $p+1$ vector $\begin{bmatrix} 1 & -a_1 & \cdots & -a_p \end{bmatrix}$.[1] We can use the `filter` function to compute the excitation function:

---

[1]MATLAB uses a different sign convention for $H(z)$.

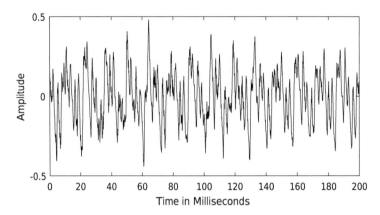

Figure 6.17: Audio signal for Example 6.6.1.

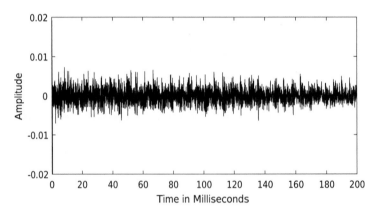

Figure 6.18: Excitation signal for Example 6.6.1.

e=**filter**(a,1,x);

and to recover the original signal from the excitation function:

x=**filter**(1,a,e);

Figure 6.18 is a plot of the excitation function for the signal in Figure 6.17.

So far, LPC has allowed us to replace N audio signal samples with N excitation signal samples and p LPC coefficients. Thus, at least in terms of sample count, LPC has not provided any benefit. However, the excitation signal can be quantized using fewer bits per sample than the original audio signal and still be used to regenerate the audio signal accurately. A proof of this statement is beyond the scope of this book, but the basic idea is that quantizing schemes can be matched to characteristics of the excitation signal to improve efficiency.

FLAC (Free Lossless Audio Coder) is a software package that compresses (i.e., reduces the size of) a PCM audio file without loss of information [38]. According to [38], the PCM audio can be recovered from the compressed file with "bit-for-bit" accuracy. One of the compression algorithms supported by FLAC is based on LPC. The audio portion of the compressed file includes the LPC coefficients and the excitation signal samples. The latter are quantized very efficiently and accurately using a coding scheme known as Rice codes [39].

6.7 Summary

This chapter has presented an overview of some filter designs of interest to audio engineers. It is far from comprehensive; for example, the subject of finite impulse response (FIR) filters is omitted. We have described the basis approach to IIR filter design (i.e., choose an appropriate analog filter design and convert it using the bilinear transform) and shown some useful examples.

MATLAB Project

Objective

Using MATLAB streaming audio tools, create a system that reads audio from a file, passes the audio through a multisection equalizer, displays the magnitude of the frequency response of the equalizer, and plays the equalized audio.

Useful MATLAB Objects

dsp.AudioFileReader Audio input source.

dsp.AudioPlayer Audio output sink.

dsp.BiquadFilter Filter object.

Previous examples illustrate the use of the audio input and output objects. The filter object can create a multisection equalizer as follows:

EQ=dsp . BiquadFilter ('SOSMatrix' , sos);

This statement creates a filter object called **EQ** based on an SOS matrix called **sos**. **sos** is an $N \times 6$ matrix of second-order filter coefficients where N is the number of sections in the equalizer. The filter object has a **step** method that filters a block of data **x** as follows:

y=step (EQ, x);

The filter object maintains internal state variables so that the result of applying the filter to a stream of blocks is equivalent to applying the filter to the entire signal in one step, which would be impractical for a long signal. The function **freqz** accepts **EQ** as an input and determines the frequency response of the filter. For example,

[h ,w]= freqz (EQ);

returns the frequency response as a complex vector **h** at 8192 equally spaced frequencies between 0 and the Nyquist frequency. These frequencies, which are in radians/second, are returned in the vector **w**. The **freqz** function also accepts the SOS matrix as an input.

Chapter 7

Audio Effect Generation

One might think that the ideal way to record music is to capture the sounds of voices and instruments with highly accurate microphones and convert them to a digital format with a high sampling rate and bit depth, without filtering or other processing of the recorded data. When we play this back using equally accurate equipment, we should reproduce the original sound, as supposedly desired. But given the history of recording or even performing music, it is clear that many artists desire to add something during the process so that the listener hears more than just a "dry" copy of the original sound. Thus, innovators over the years have come up with many ways to modify audio, either after recording or in real time during performance, to achieve a desired sound. These modifications are what we call *effects* [20].

There is no formal definition of an audio effect, so we will assume that any mechanism to modify an audio signal to produce a desired result can be called an effect. Early mechanisms to produce effects were either electronic or electromechanical. In this chapter, however, we will restrict our attention to digital signal-processing algorithms. We will also limit our coverage to a few popular effects, most of which can be implemented with linear signal-processing algorithms. One of the more complex effects, artificial reverberation, is deferred to the next chapter.

7.1   Fading

Fading is the process of gradually increasing or decreasing the amplitude of an audio signal. For example, many popular songs fade out at the end, perhaps because the composer could not think of a better ending. Cross-fading is simultaneously fading out one signal while fading in another. This may be done manually by a DJ to make a transition from one song to another. It also may be done to combine two takes of a musical passage to obtain the best of both. In this section we will review some fading and cross-fading algorithms that can be applied to discrete-time audio signals.

7.1.1 Fading In and Out

Fading can be accomplished by simply applying a fading function $F(n)$ to the audio signal $x(n)$. In the case of a fade-in, the faded signal $y(n)$ is given by

$$y(n) = \begin{cases} F_{\text{IN}}(n)x(n) & 0 \leq n < N \\ x(n) & n \geq N \end{cases} \tag{7.1}$$

where $F_{\text{IN}}(n)$ increases from 0 to 1 (usually monotonically) as n increases from 0 to $N-1$. The resulting fade-in time is $T_{\text{IN}} = (N-1)/f_s$. In the case of a fade-out, we have

$$y(n) = \begin{cases} x(n) & 0 \leq n < M \\ F_{\text{OUT}}(n-M)x(n) & M \leq n < M + N \\ 0 & n \geq M + N \end{cases} \tag{7.2}$$

where the fade-out begins at sample M and ends at sample $M+N-1$ and $F_{\text{OUT}}(n)$ decreases from 1 to 0 as n increases from 0 to $N-1$. The fade-out time is $T_{\text{OUT}} = (N-1)/f_s$.

The simplest fading function is the linear fade:

$$F_{\text{IN}}(n) = n/(N-1)$$
$$F_{\text{OUT}}(n) = 1 - n/(N-1) \tag{7.3}$$

This fading function can be implemented very easily in MATLAB using the function **linspace**. For a fade-in with (approximate) duration T:

N=**round**(fs ∗T);
Fin=**linspace** (0 ,1 ,N);
Fout=**linspace** (1 ,0 ,N);

To apply this fade-in to the beginning of signal $x(n)$:

x (1:N)=Fin.∗x (1:N);

To fade-out the end of this signal:

x (**end**–N+1:**end**)=Fout.∗x (**end**–N+1:**end**);

With a linear fading function, the *amplitude* of the signal increases or decreases linearly. Since the *power* of a signal is proportional to the square of the amplitude, we might consider the following:

$$F_{\text{IN}}(n) = \sqrt{n/(N-1)}$$
$$F_{\text{OUT}}(n) = \sqrt{1 - n/(N-1)} \tag{7.4}$$

The MATLAB versions of these fading functions are:

Fin=**sqrt** (**linspace** (0 ,1 ,N));
Fout=**sqrt** (**linspace** (1 ,0 ,N));

Other options for fading functions include exponential:

$$F_{\text{IN}}(n) = 1 - e^{-\alpha n/(N-1)}$$
$$F_{\text{OUT}}(n) = e^{-\alpha n/(N-1)} \tag{7.5}$$

where α is chosen so that $F(N-1)$ is close to 1, logarithmic:

$$F_{\text{IN}}(n) = \ln\left[1 + \frac{n}{N-1}(e-1)\right]$$

$$F_{\text{OUT}}(n) = \ln\left[e + \frac{n}{N-1}(1-e)\right] \tag{7.6}$$

and sinusoidal:

$$F_{\text{IN}}(n) = \sin\left[\frac{n\pi}{2(N-1)}\right]$$

$$F_{\text{OUT}}(n) = \cos\left[\frac{n\pi}{2(N-1)}\right] \tag{7.7}$$

The MATLAB versions of these fading functions are

Exponential

```
Fin=1-exp(-alpha*linspace(0,1,N));
Fout=exp(-alpha*linspace(0,1,N));
```

Logarithmic

```
Fin=log(linspace(1,exp(1),N));
Fout=log(linspace(exp(1),1,N));
```

Sinusoidal

```
Fin=sin(pi*linspace(0,1,N)/2);
Fout=cos(pi*linspace(0,1,N)/2);
```

Figure 7.1 shows examples of fade-in and fade-out using these nonlinear fading functions.

7.1.2   Cross-Fading

Figure 7.2 illustrates a general cross-fade situation. Two signals $x_1(n)$ and $x_2(n)$ have been aligned for a cross-fade starting at sample N_1 of $x_1(n)$ and ending just before sample N_2 of $x_1(n)$. The corresponding samples of $x_2(n)$ are M_1 and M_2, where $M_k = N_k - N_s$ and N_s is the sample offset between the two signals. The cross-faded signal $y(n)$ is constructed as follows:

$$y(n) = \begin{cases} x_1(n) & 0 \le n < N_1 \\ F_{\text{OUT}}(n-N_1)x_1(n) + F_{\text{IN}}(n-N_1)x_2(n-N_s) & N_1 \le n < N_2 \\ x_2(n-N_s) & n \ge N_2 \end{cases} \tag{7.8}$$

where the fading functions are as defined in Section 7.1.

Figure 7.3 shows how a cross-fade can be used to replace part of an audio signal. Audio signal 1 is a brief musical passage, and audio signal 2 is taken from a second version of the same passage. In this example the two signals are manually aligned in time. In the cross-faded signal the latter part of signal 1 is replaced with signal 2 using a sinusoidal cross-fade. The cross-fade begins approximately 0.05 s after the beginning of signal 2, and the fading period is approximately 0.1 s. Figure 7.4 is a close-up of the cross-fade.

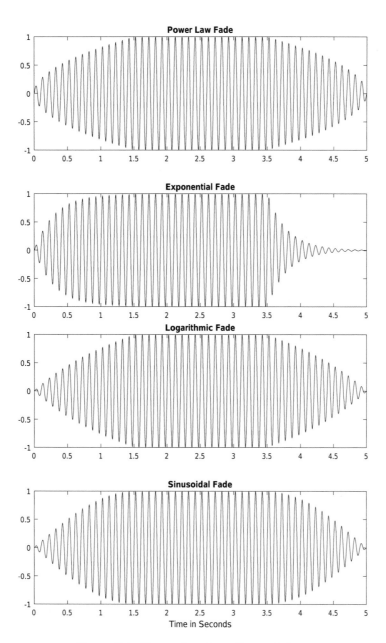

Figure 7.1: Examples of nonlinear fading.

Figure 7.2: Cross-fading two signals.

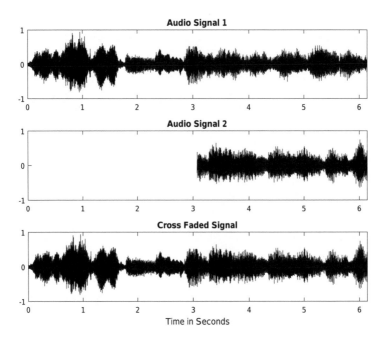

Figure 7.3: Replacing part of a signal using cross-fade.

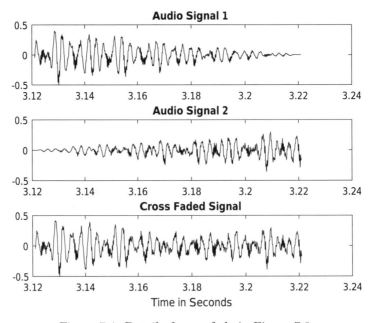

Figure 7.4: Detail of cross-fade in Figure 7.3.

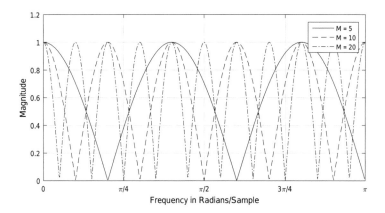

Figure 7.5: Frequency response of Equation (7.10) with $g = 0.5$.

7.2 Flanger

The flanger effect [21] is produced by combining a audio signal with a delayed version of itself where the delay is a time-varying parameter. Originally this was done by playing two identical tapes of the audio into a recorder and manually delaying the input tapes by applying pressure to the edge, or flange, of the input reels. This can now be done digitally without the need for great dexterity.

If we combine an audio signal with a delayed version of itself with a fixed delay, the input/output relation is simply

$$y(n) = (1 - g)x(n) + gx(n - M) \qquad (7.9)$$

Equation (7.9) defines a simple LTIS with a transfer function given by

$$H(z) = 1 - g + gz^{-M} \qquad (7.10)$$

Figure 7.5 is a frequency response plot of Equation (7.10) with $g = 0.5$ and a few values of M. The peaks in the plot occur at those frequencies where the delayed signal is in phase with the direct signal. And the valleys occur at those frequencies where the delayed signal is $180°$ out of phase with the direct signal. If M is time-varying, then the frequencies that are emphasized and de-emphasized will change with time, and the listener will hear this change.

A suitable time-varying delay function $M(n)$ is given by

$$M(n) = \text{round}\left[f_s(A + B \sin 2\pi f_m n / f_s)\right] \qquad (7.11)$$

The parameters in Equation (7.11) are defined in Table 7.1. $M(n)$ as defined in Equation (7.11) varies sinusoidally between $M_{\min}$ and $M_{\max}$ sampling periods with modulation frequency f_m, where

$$M_{\min} = \text{round}(f_s D_{\min})$$
$$M_{\max} = \text{round}(f_s D_{\max})$$

$$
\begin{aligned}
A &= (D_{\max} + D_{\min})/2 \\
B &= (D_{\max} - D_{\min})/2 \\
D_{\max} &= \text{maximum delay time (seconds)} \\
D_{\min} &= \text{minimum delay time (seconds)} \\
f_s &= \text{sampling frequency (hertz)} \\
f_m &= \text{modulation frequency (hertz)}
\end{aligned}
$$

Table 7.1: Parameters in Equation (7.11).

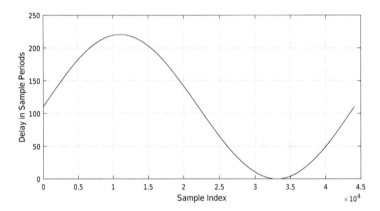

Figure 7.6: Illustration of delay function for $D_{\min} = 0$, $D_{\max} = 3$ ms, $f_s = 44\ 100$ Hz, and $f_m = 1$ Hz.

The modulation frequency is typically in the range of 1 to 5 Hz, and the maximum delay is about 10 ms. Figure 7.6 shows an example of one period of $M(n)$. For simplicity, we have forced $M(n)$ to be an integer value. This is not strictly necessary, and some implementations use interpolation to allow noninteger sample delays [20].

As we saw earlier, MATLAB makes it quite easy to set up systems to process streaming audio. With a few simple commands we can create objects to generate, process, display, and play streaming audio. In this section we will demonstrate how to add an effect to streaming audio, using the flanger as an example.

Assuming we have created an audio-file reader object **AFR** and an audio-player object **AP**, we run the following processing loop:

```
while ˜isDone(AFR)
    x=step(AFR);
    y=flanger(x,fs ,Dmin,Dmax,gain ,fm );
    step(AP, y);
end
```

Each iteration of this loop extracts a block of samples from the audio-file reader, processes the block with a flanger effect function, and passes the processed block to the audio player. The loop continues until the audio file is completely read.

The function **flanger** processes a block of samples in the array **x** using the sampling rate **fs** and the flanger parameters and returns processed samples in the array **y**. The dimensions of both **x** and **y** are either $N \times 1$ for mono or $N \times 2$ for stereo, where N is the block size. The fact that **flanger** processes a block of samples rather than the entire stream presents two issues:

- The algorithm requires access to some samples in previous blocks.

- The delay function $M(n)$ is based on the absolute sample count, not the count within the current block.

We can solve the first problem by saving the most recent $N_{\max}$ samples in a buffer, where

$$N_{\max} = \lceil f_s D_{\max} \rceil \tag{7.12}$$

The second issue can be solved by maintaining a vector of absolute sample times. Our solution is listed here:

```
function y=flanger(x, fs ,Dmin,Dmax,gain ,fm)
persistent NS NC ND T delayLine ptr
if isempty(delayLine)
    [NS,NC]=size(x);
    ND=ceil(fs*Dmax)+1; \% add 1 just to be sure!
    delayLine=zeros(ND,NC);
    ptr=0;
    t=(0:NS-1)/fs ;
end
A=(Dmax+Dmin)/2;
B=(Dmax-Dmin)/2;
y=zeros(size(x));
M=round(fs*(A+B*sin(2*pi*fm*t)));
for n=1:NS
    delayLine(ptr+1,:)=x(n,:);
    y(n,:)=(1-gain)*x(n,:)+gain*delayLine(mod(ptr-M(n),ND)+1,:);
    ptr=mod(ptr+1,ND);
end
t=t+NS/fs ;
```

The first call to `flanger` establishes some persistent variables that retain their values between successive calls. These variables include the buffer denoted `delayLine` and its associated pointer denoted `ptr`. The vector of absolute sample delays `t` is also initialized. Each call processes a block of samples as shown and then updates the absolute sample time vector.

The DSP System Toolbox also provides a straightforward means to establish a graphical user interface (GUI) to vary the effect parameters in real time as the audio is playing. The interested reader can learn more from the MATLAB Web resources.

7.3 Chorus

The chorus effect follows from the fact that even the most talented musicians can never play in precise unison [21] [23]. Consider a tenor section of a large chorus all singing the same part. Ideally each singer should sing the same word at the same pitch and at the same time as every other singer in the section. In reality, however,

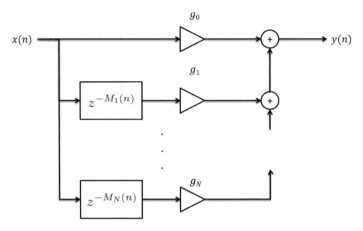

Figure 7.7: Block diagram of chorus effect system.

true unison does not happen – each voice is a little different in terms of pitch, timing, pronunciation, and other details. Fortunately, this imperfection produces a pleasing result, sometimes known as *presence*. The chorus effect attempts to produce this result so that, for example, a solo performer can have the same presence as a group.

Figure 7.7 illustrates a simple model of the chorus effect. The corresponding difference equation is

$$y(n) = g_0 x(n) + \sum_{k=1}^{N} g_k x[n - M_k(n)] \tag{7.13}$$

Equation (7.13) creates the chorus effect by combining the audio signal with N delayed versions of the signal. As in the case of the flanger, each delay $M_k(n)$ is time-varying parameter. The chorus effect model is clearly just a generalization of the flanger model and can be implemented in a similar manner using multiple delay lines and varying delays. The chorus effect uses somewhat longer delay values than the flanger effect. Also, some implementations add an element of randomness to the delays. For example, we might define the delays as

$$M_k(n) = \text{round} f_s[A + B\nu(n)] \tag{7.14}$$

where $\nu(n)$ is a low-pass noise process with a cutoff frequency of f_m.

7.4   Wah-Wah

The flanger and chorus effects are based on combining the signal with delayed versions of the same signal. The wah-wah effect is an example of an effect produced by combining the signal with a filtered version of the signal in which the filter has time-varying characteristics. For example, the filter may be a band-pass filter with a time-varying center frequency, as shown in Figure 7.8.

The band-pass filter center frequency $f_c(n)$ varies with time either according to some fixed pattern (e.g., low-frequency sinusoid) or to direct input by the performer,

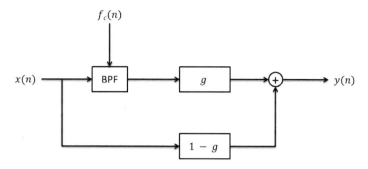

Figure 7.8: Block diagram of wah-wah effect system.

say through a pedal. The parameter g controls the blend between the original signal and the processed signal. The simple state-space filter introduced earlier [22] is a reasonable choice for our band-pass filter. Recall that it is specified by the following state equations:

$$x_H(n+1) = -\delta x_B(n) - x_L(n) + u(n)$$
$$x_B(n+1) = F_1(n)x_H(n) + y_B(n)$$
$$x_L(n+1) = F_1(n)x_B(n) + x_L(n) \tag{7.15}$$

where

$$F_1(n) = 2\sin \pi f_c(n)/f_s \tag{7.16}$$

and

$$x_B(0) = x_L(0) = 0 \tag{7.17}$$

In this version of the filter the coefficient $F_1(n)$ is time-varying. The band-pass output of the filter is given by

$$y(n) = x_B(n) \tag{7.18}$$

Example 7.4.1. The following MATLAB script implements a wah-wah effect with sinusoidal modulation of the band-pass filter center frequency.

```
blockSize=8000;
AFR=dsp.AudioFileReader('Dreams_I_Never_See.m4a',...
    'SamplesPerFrame',blockSize);
AP=dsp.AudioPlayer;
fs=AFR.SampleRate;
Fmax=1500; Fmin=500; fm=0.5; damp=0.05; gain=0.5;
A=(Fmax+Fmin)/2;
B=(Fmax-Fmin)/2;
t=(0:blockSize-1)/fs;
clear wahwah;
while ~isDone(AFR)
    u=step(AFR);
    fc=A+B*sin(2*pi*fm*t);
    y=wahwah(u,fs,fc,damp,gain);
```

```
        step(AP,y);
        t=t+blockSize/fs;
end
release(AP);
```

In this implementation we compute the time-varying center frequency and pass it to the wah-wah filter function as an argument. The wah-wah filter implementation is listed here:

```
function y=wahwah(u,fs,fc,damp,gain)
[Ns,Nc]=size(u);
persistent xB xL
if isempty(xB)
    xB=zeros(1,Nc);
    xL=zeros(1,Nc);
end
y=zeros(size(u));
for n=1:Ns
    F1=2*sin(pi*fc(n)/fs);
    xH=-xL-damp*xB+u(n,:);
    xB=F1*xH+xB;
    xL=F1*xB+xL;
    y(n,:)=gain*xB+(1-gain)*u(n,:);
end
```

This function processes successive blocks of samples contained in the Ns by Nc input matrix u, where Ns is the number of samples in the block and Nc is the number of channels. The vector fc contains Ns center frequency values. The state variables xB and xL are initialized on the first function call.

7.5   Dynamic Range Control

The dynamic range of an audio signal is the ratio, expressed as a base 10 logarithm, of the maximum-to-minimum signal amplitude [36]. In an ideal listening environment, we might want to preserve the dynamic range to match that of the original sound, but under some circumstances it may be desirable to compress or expand the range. In a noisy environment such as a moving vehicle or a facility only partially dedicated to musical sound, we may be faced with the choice of either being unable to hear the quiet segments or unable to bear the loud segments. Dynamic range control is a solution to this dilemma.

Dynamic range control can be specified with a deceptively simple equation:

$$y(n) = g(n)x(n - M) \tag{7.19}$$

where $x(n)$ is the input signal, $y(n)$ is the output signal, and $g(n)$ is a varying gain. Note that because of the M sample delay, the gain applied to each sample can be based on samples that follow, giving the system a predictive property. So how do we determine the gain $g(n)$? We will first consider the case of dynamic range compression.

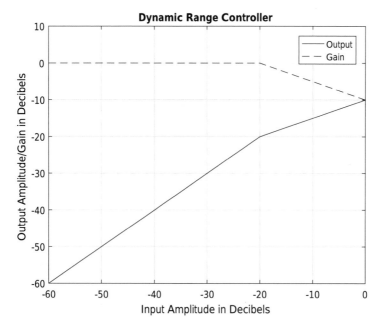

Figure 7.9: Static input/output curve: dynamic range compression.

Figure 7.9 is an example of a static input/output and gain curves for a dynamic range compressor. If the input amplitude in decibels (we will see how to calculate this shortly) is below the *compressor threshold* (−20 dB in this example), then the gain is 0 dB, and the output signal amplitude matches that of the input. If the input amplitude exceeds the compressor threshold, however, then the gain decreases, and the output amplitude increases more slowly than the input amplitude. As a result, the dynamic range is reduced by 10 dB.

The static curves can be specified in terms of a compression threshold X_{CO} and a slope S as

$$Y_{\text{DB}} = \begin{cases} X_{\text{DB}} & X_{\text{DB}} \leq X_{\text{CO}} \\ S(X_{\text{DB}} - X_{\text{CO}}) + X_{\text{CO}} & X_{\text{DB}} > X_{\text{CO}} \end{cases} \tag{7.20}$$

and

$$G_{\text{DB}} = \begin{cases} 0 & X_{\text{DB}} \leq X_{\text{CO}} \\ (S - 1)(X_{\text{DB}} - X_{\text{CO}}) & X_{\text{DB}} > X_{\text{CO}} \end{cases} \tag{7.21}$$

where X_{DB} and Y_{DB} are the input and output amplitudes in decibels. Note that compression occurs only if $S < 1$. For $S = 1$, the gain remains 0 dB above the threshold, so there is no effect. If $S = 0$, the compressor acts as a *limiter*, and the output amplitude does not exceed the threshold value. If $S > 1$, the device becomes an *expander*, giving a boost to signals above the threshold. Finally, we have the extreme case of $S = -\infty$, making the device a *gate*. In this case the gate normally applies when the input amplitude is below the threshold. See [36] more more detail on these variations.

The input amplitude X_{DB} is based on either a peak or RMS value; we will examine the latter. The mean squared amplitude based on the most recent L

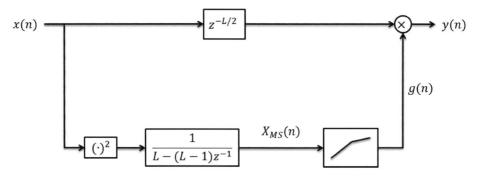

Figure 7.10: Dynamic range compressor block diagram.

samples is given by

$$X_{MS}(n) = \frac{1}{L} \sum_{k=0}^{L-1} x(n-k)^2 \tag{7.22}$$

This can be approximated reasonably well with a more efficient recursive formula:

$$X_{MS}(n) = \frac{L-1}{L} X_{MS}(n-1) + \frac{1}{L} x(n)^2 \tag{7.23}$$

In either case, we can take $X_{MS}(n)$ as a measure of the signal power associated with sample $x(n - L/2)$, since it is based on L samples centered around this sample. Thus, we set the delay to $M = L/2$.

To determine the gain associated with a given value of $X_{MS}(n)$, we have to convert to decibels as

$$X_{DB}(n) = 10 \log_{10} X_{MS}(n) \tag{7.24}$$

Our static curve is based on a maximum amplitude of 0 dB. In a MATLAB implementation in which samples are obtained from a library function such as **audioread**, the samples are normalized such that $-1 \leq x(n) \leq 1$ and the computed decibel amplitude will always be 0 or less. In general, some normalization or other adjustment may be needed to make the signal amplitude consistent with the range of the static curves.

Figure 7.10 shows how the static curve of Figure 7.9 and the dynamic calculation of Equation (7.23) go together to construct a dynamic range compressor. The output $y(n)$ is the product of the gain $g(n)$ and a delayed sample $x(n - L/2)$. The gain is determined by Equation (7.21), converting X_{MS} to dB and converting the dB gain $G(n)$ to $g(n)$. Equation (7.23) is represented in the figure by the corresponding z-transform.

Example 7.5.1. The following MATLAB script is an implementation of the dynamic range compressor shown in Figure 7.10.

```
[x,fs]=audioread('Same_Old_Lines.wav');
[N,~]=size(x);
Xco=-20;
slope=0.5;
T=10;
```

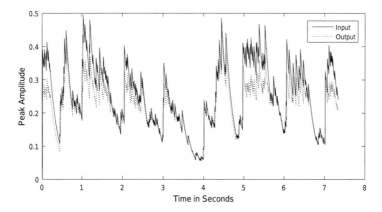

Figure 7.11: Peak amplitude of original and compressed signals.

```
L=round(fs*T/1000);
K=round(L/2);
x=[zeros(K,1); x];
damp=(L−1)/L;
x2=0;
y=zeros(N,1);
for n=1:N
    x2=damp*x2+(1−damp)*x(K+n)^2;
    Xdb=10*log10(x2);
    if (Xdb<=Xco)
        G=0;
    else
        G=(slope −1)*(Xdb−Xco);
    end
    y(n)=x(n)*10^(G/20);
end
```

The script obtains samples from a small audio file. The compression threshold and slope are set to −20 dB and 0.5, respectively. The value of the averaging range L is derived from an averaging time T, which is set to 10 ms. The delay is established by prepending $L/2$ zeros to the vector of samples. The main loop updates the input RMS and computes the gain and the output. Figure 7.11 displays the result in terms of the peak amplitudes of the input and the output.

Dynamic range control is one example of *nonlinear* audio signal processing; the static curves are not linear functions. Nonlinear systems generally introduce distortion, which at first may seem undesirable. But we have given the rationale for dynamic range control, and we can therefore view it as a beneficial distortion. Several other examples of nonlinear audio signal processing can be found in [20].

7.6   Tempo Change and Pitch Shifting

The ability to vary independently the tempo or pitch of a recording is often useful. For example, a musician may wish to practice or perform with recorded accompaniment but would like to adjust this accompaniment to match his or her vocal range or playing ability. In this section we will present some basic methods, taken mainly from [10] and [20], for varying the tempo and pitch of an audio signal.

Note that the tempo and pitch of an audio signal can easily be changed by restating the sampling rate. That is, the playback system can process the samples at a faster or slower rate. But this does not change the tempo and pitch *independently*. Instead, the pitch changes in direct proportion to the tempo, just as it does if you increase or decrease the speed of the turntable on your grandfather's hi-fi. We will only consider, therefore, methods that change only the tempo or only the pitch.

7.6.1   Time Domain Methods

We will first consider methods based on direct modification of the time domain signal. These methods are similar to but somewhat simpler than those presented in [20]. We will assume that the signal is available as a sequence of blocks $\mathbf{x}(m)$ of N samples. Figure 7.12 shows three consecutive sample blocks in varying degrees of alignment, with cross-fades indicated by diagonal lines. In Figure 7.12a block $\mathbf{x}(m)$ is cross-faded with itself, resulting in no change in the block. In Figure 7.12b block $\mathbf{x}(m)$ is cross-faded with a delayed copy of itself, resulting in stretching the block by up to N samples. In Figure 7.12c the head each block is cross-faded with the tail of its successor. This can reduce the sample count by up to $N/2$ samples per block without reaching the point of multiple overlaps. Increasing the number of samples as in Figure 7.12b will decrease the tempo, while decreasing the number of samples as in Figure 7.12c will increase the tempo.

First consider tempo reduction (Figure 7.12b), in which we simply stretch each block to create some artificial samples in the middle of the block. In this case we can process each input block $\mathbf{x}(m)$ to produce an expanded block $\mathbf{y}(m)$. The number of samples N_y in the expanded block is given by

$$N_y = \text{round}(\alpha N) \tag{7.25}$$

where α is a tempo change factor $(1 < \alpha < 2)$. The samples in the expanded block are calculated as

$$y(n) = \begin{cases} x(n) & n < N_y - N \\ F_{\text{OUT}} \cdot x(n) + F_{\text{IN}} \cdot x(n - N_y + N) & N_y - N \leq n < N \\ x(n - N_y + N) & N \leq n < N_y \end{cases} \tag{7.26}$$

where the block index m has been omitted for clarity.

To increase the tempo we can overlap successive blocks as in Figure 7.12c. The number of samples in our contracted block is still given by Equation (7.25) but with the tempo change factor in the range $0.5 < \alpha < 1$. Contracted block $\mathbf{y}(m)$ consists of a cross-fade of the tail of block $\mathbf{x}(m-1)$ and the head of block $\mathbf{x}(m)$ followed by

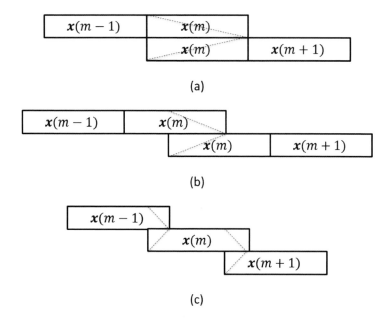

Figure 7.12: Tempo change by overlapping blocks.

subsequent samples of block $\mathbf{x}(m)$, excluding its tail. Specifically:

$$
y(m,n) = \begin{cases} F_{\text{IN}} \cdot x(m,n) + F_{\text{OUT}} \cdot x(m-1, n+N_y) & 0 \le n < N - N_y \\ x(m,n) & N - N_y \le n < N_y \end{cases} \tag{7.27}
$$

Although this approach to tempo changing is quite heuristic, it works reasonably well, as the student can verify by completing the associated MATLAB project at the end of this chapter. Moreover, the change in tempo can easily be converted to a shift in pitch by simply resampling the expanded or contracted blocks to restore the number of samples per block to N. If the tempo has been reduced by expanding the blocks, resampling will restore the original tempo, but will increase the pitch by a factor α. Similarly, if the tempo has been increased by contracting the blocks, resampling will restore the original tempo and decrease the pitch by a factor α. This can also be verified via the MATLAB exercise.

7.6.2 Frequency Domain Methods

We can also vary the tempo and pitch of an audio signal by modifying the signal's spectrum. Our basic procedure is (1) compute the STFT of the signal, (2) modify the STFT, and (3) recover the signal using the inverse STFT. We will again assume that the audio signal is a sequence of blocks of N samples, and we will compute the STFT based on a Hanning window of length $2N$ with 50% overlap. The STFT of the mth block is

$$
\mathbf{S}(m) = \text{DFT}\left\{ \mathbf{w} \cdot \begin{bmatrix} \mathbf{x}(m-1) & \mathbf{x}(m) \end{bmatrix} \right\} \tag{7.28}
$$

To recover $\mathbf{x}(m)$, we first compute the IDFT of $\mathbf{S}(m)$.

$$\begin{aligned} \mathbf{s}(m) &= \text{IDFT}[\mathbf{S}(m)] \\ &= \begin{bmatrix} \mathbf{w}_1 \cdot \mathbf{x}(m-1) & \mathbf{w}_2 \cdot \mathbf{x}(m) \end{bmatrix} \\ &= \begin{bmatrix} \mathbf{s}_1(m) & \mathbf{s}_2(m) \end{bmatrix} \end{aligned} \qquad (7.29)$$

where $\mathbf{w}_1$ and $\mathbf{w}_2$ are the lower and upper halves of the Hanning window, respectively. Then $\mathbf{x}(m)$ is

$$\mathbf{x}(m) = \mathbf{s}_2(m) + \mathbf{s}_1(m+1) \qquad (7.30)$$

Let $\mathbf{S}$ be the STFT of a given block, dropping the block index for clarity. $\mathbf{S}$ contains $2N$ samples of a frequency domain function covering the frequency range $0 \le f \le f_s$. These frequency domain samples correspond to $2N$ time domain samples covering a period of time of duration $T = 2N/f_s$. Now compute a modified STFT $\mathbf{S}'$ as

$$\mathbf{S}' = \text{LRES}(\mathbf{S}, L) \qquad (7.31)$$

where LRES is a function that resamples $\mathbf{S}$ to L samples based on linear interpolation. These samples still cover the frequency range $0 \le f \le f_s$, but the corresponding time period is now of duration $T' = L/f_s$. Thus, when we play the recovered signal without changing f_s, the pitch is not changed, but the tempo is either increased ($L < 2N$) or decreased ($L > 2N$). On the other hand, if we resample the recovered signal back to $2N$ samples, we will maintain the original tempo but scale the frequency range to $0 \le f \le 2Nf_s/L$, thus changing the pitch by a factor of $2N/L$.

Note that one should use caution when artificially modifying the STFT. Recall that the DFT exhibits conjugate symmetry for a real signal in that components for negative frequencies are the complex conjugates of the components of the corresponding positive frequencies. Equation (7.31) may violate this condition; thus it is prudent to adjust the artificial STFT to enforce conjugate symmetry.

7.6.3 Limitations of the Basic Tempo and Pitch Change Methods

The methods presented in this section are straightforward and suggest some basic approaches to modifying the tempo and pitch of an audio signal. However, a greater degree of sophistication may be desired, especially in the case of pitch shifting. The phase vocoder [35], which uses phase information to provide more accurate estimates of the dominant frequencies in the signal spectrum, is one recommended approach.

Both the time and frequency domain methods presented here are based on changing the pitch by simply scaling the frequency spectrum. This is not a good model of real instruments or voices. Consider, for example, an acoustic guitar. It is quite common to change the overall pitch of the instrument by applying a capo, which effectively shortens the strings and thereby raises the pitch. If the capo is placed on the second fret and the player strums a G chord, the result will be an A chord. But note that the only significant change is the shortening of the strings; the rest of the guitar, which acts as a frequency-shaping filter, is unchanged. Thus, the spectrum of the A chord will generally not be just a scaled version of the spectrum of the G

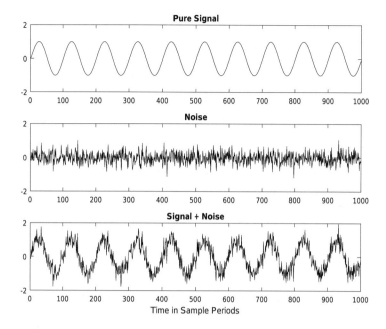

Figure 7.13: Audio signal corrupted by noise.

chord. Simply scaling the frequency spectrum is more like shrinking or expanding the entire guitar, not just the strings.

The STFT or some variation such as the phase vocoder, is a logical tool for tempo and pitch manipulation. However, in order to maintain the character of the actual instrument (including the voice), we need to include some model of the mechanism that produces the sound.

7.7 Noise Reduction

In practice, audio signals are seldom pure. Any practical system for processing sound will record or introduce spurious signals that corrupt the desired signal and reduce the quality of the resulting audio. We call this kind of corruption *noise* and seek ways to avoid it or remove it from the signal. Figure 7.13 shows a pure sinusoidal signal, a noise signal, and a combination of the two. In Chapter 6 we showed that a low-pass filter can partially eliminate noise without seriously distorting the signal. In this section we will consider a more elaborate approach.

We can state the problem mathematically as follows: Given a signal $x(n)$ that is some combination of a pure signal $s(n)$ and a noise signal $w(n)$, determine an estimate $\hat{s}(n)$ of the pure signal. That is, given

$$x(n) = f[s(n), w(n)] \qquad (7.32)$$

determine an estimate of the pure signal based on $x(n)$, i.e.,

$$\hat{s}(n) = g[x(n)] \qquad (7.33)$$

Unfortunately this problem is far easier to state that to solve. Thus, we will begin to simplify the problem by assuming that the noise is additive, i.e.,

$$x(n) = s(n) + w(n) \tag{7.34}$$

This assumption is both reasonable and helpful, but the problem is still quite complex. We cannot obtain $s(n)$ by simply subtracting $w(n)$ from $x(n)$, because the noise signal $w(n)$ is unknown and unpredictable. Thus, we have to settle for an estimate $\hat{s}(n)$ based on incomplete knowledge of the noise signal.

7.7.1   Noise Process

A noise signal is most often modeled as a random process (or, if you prefer a fancier name, a *stochastic* process). A complete and rigorous discussion of random processes is beyond the scope of this book, and so we will limit our discussion to a few basic properties.

In the discrete time domain, a random process is a sequence of random variables. Let us assume that this sequence is produced by a magic box. We do not know what is in the box, we just know that at the end of each sample period it ejects a sample $w(n)$. Before we observe the first sample $w(0)$, we may only know that the sample will be some real number. But as we observe more and more samples, we may see some patterns emerge. For example, we may notice that the sample values rarely fall outside a certain range. We may also measure the average sample value as

$$\overline{w} = \frac{1}{N} \sum_{n=0}^{N-1} w(n) \tag{7.35}$$

or the average sample power as

$$\overline{w^2} = \frac{1}{N} \sum_{n=0}^{N-1} |w(n)|^2 \tag{7.36}$$

What can these observations and measurements tell us about future values of $w(n)$? If N is sufficiently large and the noise process is *stationary*, measurements like $\overline{w}$ and $\overline{w^2}$ based on N values of $w(n)$ starting with $n = n_0$ will not vary greatly with n_0. Thus, we can assume that for a stationary noise process, measurements based on any sequence of N consecutive noise samples apply reasonably well to the entire signal. For at least some degree of simplicity, we will assume that the noise process is stationary.

The *power spectral density* (PSD) is a more complex measurement of a signal based on the DFT and is a key to noise removal. Let $\mathbf{x}$ be a signal of length N and $\mathbf{X}$ be the corresponding DFT (recall the notation introduced in discussion of the STFT in Chapter 5). From Parseval's theorem we have

$$\sum_{n=0}^{N-1} |x(n)|^2 = \frac{1}{N} \sum_{k=0}^{N-1} |X(k)|^2 \tag{7.37}$$

From Equation (7.37) we can derive an expression for average signal power $\overline{x^2}$:

$$\overline{x^2} = \frac{1}{N} \sum_{n=0}^{N-1} |x(n)|^2$$

$$= \frac{1}{N^2} \sum_{k=0}^{N-1} |X(k)|^2$$

$$= \frac{1}{N} \sum_{k=0}^{N-1} P_x(k) \qquad (7.38)$$

where

$$P_x(k) = \frac{1}{N} |X(k)|^2 \qquad (7.39)$$

is the PSD.

Estimating the PSD of a noise signal requires a bit more work. If $\mathbf{w}$ is a block of samples from a noise signal, then the DFT $\mathbf{W}$ and the PSD $\mathbf{P}_w$ are also random and may vary significantly from block to block. Thus, we need to derive some kind of average PSD from multiple blocks of noise samples. This can be accomplished using the Welch method as described in [10]. The Welch method is similar to the STFT in that we compute the PSD from a sequence of windowed, overlapping blocks of samples. Let $\mathbf{w}(m)$ be the mth block of N samples and let $\mathbf{W}(m)$ be the DFT of this block with window $\mathbf{v}$, i.e.,

$$\mathbf{W}(m) = \text{DFT}[\mathbf{w}(m) \cdot \mathbf{v}] \qquad (7.40)$$

where the dot notation is as defined in Chapter 5. We can convert $\mathbf{W}(m)$ to $\mathbf{P}_w(m)$ using Equation (7.39). The average PSD is then given by

$$\mathbf{P}_w = \frac{1}{M} \sum_{m=0}^{M-1} \mathbf{P}_w(m) \qquad (7.41)$$

where M is the number of blocks. Fortunately, the good people at MATLAB have packaged all of this complexity in an easy-to-use function called `pwelch`.

Example 7.7.1. The following MATLAB script uses the function `wgn` to generate a noise signal and the function `pwelch` to calculate the PSD.

```
N=512;
x=wgn(100*N,1,0);
[P,w]=pwelch(x,N,N/2,'twosided');
plot(w,10*log10(2*pi*P))
```

The block size is set to $N = 512$. The call to function `wgn` produces a column vector of $100N$ random numbers to simulate a noise signal. This vector is the first argument of the function `pwelch`. The next two arguments are the block size and the number of overlap samples. The return values are the PSD and a vector of the normalized frequencies ranging from 0 to 2π. We make some adjustment because of the convention of `pwelch` to normalize the PSD by the sampling frequency f_s with a default value of 2π Hz. Figure 7.14 is a plot of the result.

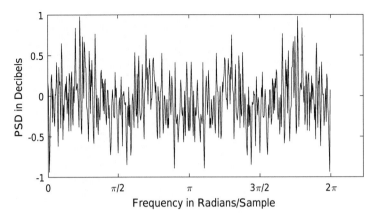

Figure 7.14: PSD of a noise signal.

The MATLAB function `wgn` generates an approximation of *white Gaussian noise*, a popular noise model. In simple terms, white Gaussian noise has two primary characteristics:

- Each sample in the sequence is a Gaussian (also known as normally distributed) random variable.

- Each sample in the sequence is independent of all the other samples.

The first characteristic determines the probability that the value of the sample will fall within a given range. The Gaussian distribution is completely specified by two parameters: the mean μ and the standard deviation σ. A Gaussian random variable tends not to stray more than a few times σ from the mean. Function `wgn` sets the mean to 0 and sets the standard deviation according to the third input parameter. The second characteristic makes white noise especially erratic and unpredictable. Sample n can be radically different from sample $n - 1$; the past tells you nothing about the future.

In practice we must somehow obtain a sample of the noise process. One common method is to look for a noise-only segment of a noisy audio signal, perhaps at the beginning or end of a recording. After obtaining the noise PSD from this segment, we can then create a noise filter, as described in the next section.

7.7.2   Noise Filtering

In this section we will review some basic methods to reduce additive noise using a linear filter function. We will assume that the noise signal is a stationary random process.

In the frequency domain Equation (7.34) becomes

$$X(k, n) = S(k, n) + W(k) \tag{7.42}$$

where $X(k, n)$ and $S(k, n)$ are the STFTs (frequency bin k and block time n) of the noisy signal $x(n)$ and the noise-free signal $s(n)$, respectively. The estimated STFT of the noise-free signal is given by

$$\hat{S}(k, n) = H(k, n)X(k, n) \tag{7.43}$$

where $H(k, n)$ is a suitable filter function. The noise-reduced signal $\hat{s}(n)$ is the inverse STFT of $\hat{S}(k, n)$. Some common methods to determine $H(k, n)$ are mentioned in [31]. The Wiener noise-reduction filter, so named because of its origin in the classic work of N. Wiener [32], is given by

$$H_W(k, n) = \max \left[\frac{P_x(k, n) - P_w(k)}{P_x(k, n)}, 0 \right] \tag{7.44}$$

A method known as *spectral subtraction* uses a similar filter:

$$H_{SS}(k, n) = \max \left[\frac{\sqrt{P_x(k, n)} - \sqrt{P_w(k)}}{\sqrt{P_x(k, n)}}, 0 \right] \tag{7.45}$$

Both of these filters either eliminate or attenuate the part of the spectrum where the total signal power is on the order of or less than the noise power. Both methods are able to reduce noise significantly without losing much of the desired signal. However, they can introduce artifacts known as musical or tonal noise. These artifacts may be combated by smoothing the filter function to avoid large discontinuities between frequency or time steps. The more complex Ephraim and Malah filter [33], which we will not discuss, is much less prone to these artifacts.

7.7.3   MATLAB Implementation

The following is the main loop of a MATLAB script implementation of a Wiener noise-reduction method:

```
while ~isDone(AFR)
    x=step(AFR)+wgn(N/2,1,-20);
    S=fft([xold; x].*window);
    Ps=(abs(S).^2)/N;
    H=max([Ps-Pw zeros(N,1)],[],2)./Ps;
    s=real(ifft(H.*S));
    y=y+s;
    step(AP,y(1:N/2));
    xold=x;
    y=[y(N/2+1:end); zeros(N/2,1)];
end
```

Each iteration of the loop proceeds as follows:

- Get next $N/2$ samples from the audio-file reader and add white Gaussian noise. The estimated PSD of this noise process `Pw` has already been calculated.

- Calculate the STFT `S` and the PSD `Ps` of the current signal block, which consists of the most recent N samples.

- Calculate the filter coefficients `H`.

- Apply the filter coefficients to the STFT and then calculate the inverse STFT. Send a block of $N/2$ noise-reduced samples to the audio player.

- Prepare for next iteration.

We calculate the STFT using the Hanning window and 50% overlap, thus allowing straightforward calculation of the inverse STFT. For consistency of comparison, we also use the Hanning window to calculate the noise signal PSD. The call to `pwelch` in this case is

Pw=2*$\mathbf{pi}$*pwelch(wgn(10*N,1,−20),window,N/2,'twosided');

7.8   Summary

In this chapter we have continued to apply our knowledge of audio signal processing to analyze and implement some popular audio effects. We went a few steps beyond LTIS, first introducing time-varying parameters and finally permitting nonlinearity. And we looked at some implementations using MATLAB streaming audio, which can apply the effects in real time.

Our review is far from comprehensive, and new effects become available on a regular basis. An organization known as DAFX (`http://www.dafx.de`) has been particularly active in hosting conferences and publishing research about digital audio effects [20, 40]. DAFX also provides MATLAB implementations of advanced audio effects via their website at `http://ant-s4.unibw-hamburg.de/dafx/DAFX_Book_Page_2nd_edition/matlab.html`.

MATLAB Projects

Chorus

Modify the script and function for the flanger effect to implement the chorus effect with $N = 2$.

Dynamic Range Compression

Modify the script of Example 7.5.1 to a streaming audio version that reads from a normal-sized wave file and plays the compressed audio.

Tempo and Pitch Change

Write and test a MATLAB streaming audio script to shift the pitch up or down by up to 6 semitones. Shifting the pitch by n semitones is equivalent to changing the pitch by a factor of α where

$$\alpha = 2^{n/12}$$

Use the frequency domain method described in Section 7.6.2. The script should include:

- An audio-file reader to provide blocks of audio samples

- An audio player to play the shifted audio

- A processing loop to compute, manipulate and invert the STFT and manipulate and play the resulting signal. At each iteration the STFT is applied to the two most recent blocks using a Hanning window.

Noise Removal

Complete the script for the Wiener noise-reduction system and test it on an audio recording. Compare three scenarios based on listening to the output:

- Recording with no added noise

- Recording with added noise but no noise reduction

- Recording with added noise and noise reduction

Note any artifacts introduced by the noise-reduction system.

Chapter 8

Reverberation

When you hear music played in a acoustically well-designed concert hall, church, or other large space, the various sounds are sustained such that the more recent sounds are blended with remnants of previous sounds to give the listener a feeling for the dynamics of the sound in both time and space. The impulsive sound of, say, a starter's pistol, which might sound like a short loud "pop" in an open field, may be heard for several seconds in a "live" hall. The basic reason for this is that in an enclosed space with reflective surfaces, sound travels from the source to the listener over multiple paths, and each path can have a unique combination of delay, attenuation, and frequency shaping. The delay depends on the length of the path, and a path including many reflections will have noticeably more delay than a direct path from the source to the listener. Attenuation and frequency shaping depend on characteristics of the reflecting surfaces and acoustic properties of the atmosphere in the performance space. The goal here is to design a digital filter that can simulate the effect of a reverberant space on audio. In particular, we wish to design a digital filter that has an impulse response similar to that of a (perhaps particular) reverberant space.

One straightforward approach is to measure the impulse response of a reverberant space and use this measured response to process an audio signal via convolution. This approach has been made practical by the development of fast convolution algorithms, such as the overlap-add method discussed in Chapter 4. Moreover, robust measurement techniques, especially the swept-sine method [16], provide excellent replications of the impulse responses of real spaces.

Other approaches attempt to mimic the impulse response of a reverberant space without explicitly measuring it. For example, one might proceed as follows:

- Determine some basic characteristics of the impulse response of a reverberant space.

- Design a digital filter with an impulse response that has those characteristics

- Leave some filter parameters open for the listener to adjust to his or her liking.

The impulse response $h(n)$ of a reverberant space has the following characteristics:

- $h(n) = 0$ for $n < 0$ (realizable).

130

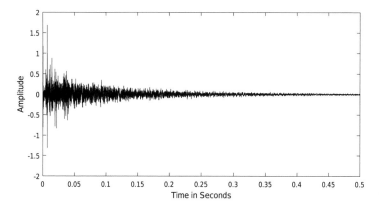

Figure 8.1: Impulse response of small church outside Amsterdam [12].

- $h(n)$ generally (but not necessarily consistently) decreases exponentially with increasing n.

- Density of nonzero $h(n)$ increases with increasing n.

The second characteristic reflects the fact that the sound energy is eventually absorbed by the space; the exponential nature of the decay was initially described by Sabine [24]. The third characteristic follows from the fact that the first "copies" of the impulse to reach the listener follow a small number of relatively straightforward paths involving only a few reflections. With passing time, however, the impulse copies find more and more ways to reach the listener, and their arrival rate increases, ultimately resembling a statistical noise process. These two phases of the response are often referred to as *early reflections* and *late reverberation*, respectively.

8.1 Swept-Sine Measurement of Impulse Response

Suppose we would like to model the audio path between point A and point B in some environment as an LTIS. If we can create an impulse at point A and record the response at point B, then we obtain the impulse response. So we might, for example, fire a starter's pistol, which makes a very loud sound with very short duration, at point A. The result of such a recording is displayed in Figure 8.1, and indeed it resembles an impulse response. Unfortunately this simple approach is not very robust, and the results can be distorted by ambient noise and nonlinearities. Recent research has led to a preference for a *swept-sine* method [16], which largely overcomes these problems. We will present here an overview of this method.

In accordance with its name, the swept-sine method applies a swept-sine wave to the system of interest, records the system response, and uses the result to determine the system's impulse response. In the continuous time domain, a general swept-sine signal is given by

$$x(t) = \sin \phi(t) \tag{8.1}$$

where $\phi(t)$ is chosen to produce an exponential sweep between two frequencies f_1 and f_2 during a time period of length T. For a general exponential sweep, $\phi(t)$ is given by

$$\phi(t) = A(e^{t/\tau} - 1) \qquad (8.2)$$

The instantaneous radian frequency $\omega(t)$ is given by

$$\omega(t) = \frac{d\phi(t)}{dt}$$
$$= \frac{A}{\tau} e^{t/\tau} \qquad (8.3)$$

Given that the desired frequencies at $t = 0$ and $t = T$ are ω_1 and ω_2, respectively ($\omega_k = 2\pi f_k$), we have

$$\omega_1 = \frac{A}{\tau}$$
$$\omega_2 = \frac{A}{\tau} e^{T/\tau} \qquad (8.4)$$

so that

$$\tau = \frac{T}{\ln(\omega_2/\omega_1)}$$
$$A = \omega_1 \tau \qquad (8.5)$$

The digital swept-sine signal $x(n)$ is simply a sampled version of $x(t)$.

Now let us define an inverse $x^{-1}(n)$ such that

$$x(n) * x^{-1}(n) = \delta(n) \qquad (8.6)$$

If $y(n)$ is the LTIS response to $x(n)$ we can write

$$y(n) * x^{-1}(n) = h(n) * x(n) * x^{-1}(n)$$
$$= h(n) * \delta(n) = h(n) \qquad (8.7)$$

Thus, we can determine the impulse response of an LTIS by convolving the signal response with the inverse signal. The inverse signal corresponding to the swept-sine signal is given by

$$x^{-1}(t) = \frac{\omega_1}{2\pi\tau} e^{-t/\tau} x(-t) \qquad (8.8)$$

The digital version is again obtained by sampling. Figure 8.2 illustrates the first second of a swept-sine signal sweeping from 20 Hz to 20 000 Hz over a period of 3 s. This signal was generated by a MATLAB function called synthSweep developed at Oygo Sound LLC and available from the MATLAB Central File Exchange along with a companion function called extractIR to determine the system impulse response from the system's response to the swept-sine signal.

Figure 8.3 displays the impulse response measured in the Great Hall at the Mile End campus of Queen Mary, University of London. This is one of many measured impulse responses in a database maintained by the Centre for Digital Music at the university [18]. We will use this impulse response to illustrate the how the swept-sine signal and its inverse can be used to measure the impulse response of a space.

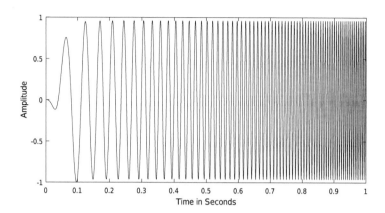

Figure 8.2: Swept-sine signal.

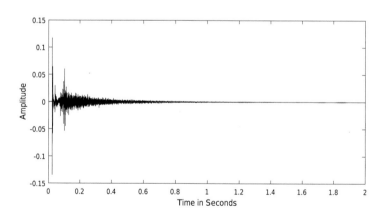

Figure 8.3: Sample Great Hall impulse response.

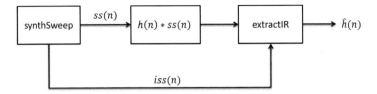

Figure 8.4: System to measure impulse response.

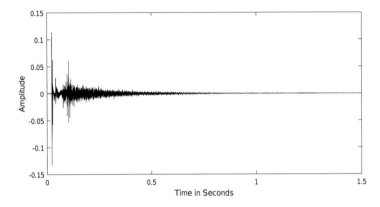

Figure 8.5: Extracted impulse response.

Figure 8.4 illustrates the basic approach. We use `synthSweep` to generate a swept-sine signal and apply it to our system. For the purpose of this illustration, we will simply calculate the convolution of the swept-sine and the impulse response. In practice, we would feed the swept-sine function to a loudspeaker at location A and record the sound at location B. The `extractIR` function requires two inputs, the swept-sine response of the system and the inverse swept-sine function, which is nicely provided by `synthSweep`. The `extractIR` function calculates an estimate of the system impulse response. Figure 8.5 is a plot of the estimated impulse response, which is a good match to the original shown in Figure 8.3.

A reverb effect generated using a measured impulse response has the advantage of being related to a real space. It can transport any performance to that space! However, the structures of some of the available databases betray some of the disadvantages. Typically a given space is represented by dozens or even more than 100 different impulse responses. For example, there may be responses for various combinations source and listener locations. Examination of even a few sample responses shows that they vary considerably. Nevertheless, the combination of fast convolution and measured impulse response is one of the available and practical choices for creating artificial reverberation.

8.2 Reverb Effect Building Blocks

A number of methods have been developed to create an LTIS with an impulse response that has the characteristics of a reverberant space. Many of these use combinations of a few basic filters, especially *comb filters* and *all-pass filters*. We will first introduce these filters along with some other building blocks and then look at various combinations of these filters that simulate a reverberant space.

8.2.1 Delay Line

Delay lines can be used to introduce time delays corresponding to the times required for sound to propagate between points of reflection in a space. In the digital domain a time delay translates to a sample delay, i.e., a given number of sampling intervals. The transfer function of a time delay corresponding to N sampling intervals is simply

$$H(z) = z^{-N} \tag{8.9}$$

This simple transfer function models pure delay with no attenuation or frequency-shaping. We can add frequency-dependent attenuation by using a slightly more complex transfer function:

$$H(z) = A(z)z^{-N} \tag{8.10}$$

We will refer this as a *damped delay line*. For example, $A(z)$ can be a simple low-pass filter:

$$A(z) = \frac{g}{1 - dz^{-1}} \tag{8.11}$$

We will refer to g and d as the gain and damping factors, respectively. The magnitude of $A(z)$ in Equation (8.11) varies from A_{LF} at $f = 0$ to A_{HF} at $f = f_s/2$ where

$$A_{\text{LF}} = \frac{g}{1 - d}$$
$$A_{\text{HF}} = \frac{g}{1 + d} \tag{8.12}$$

We can invert Equation (8.12) to determine g and d:

$$d = \frac{A_{\text{LF}} - A_{\text{HF}}}{A_{\text{LF}} + A_{\text{HF}}}$$
$$g = \frac{2A_{\text{LF}}A_{\text{HF}}}{A_{\text{LF}} + A_{\text{HF}}} \tag{8.13}$$

The magnitude of $A(z)$ should also vary with the length of the delay $T_D = N/f_s$. We will assume an exponential decrease such that A_{LF} and A_{HF} can be expressed as

$$A_{\text{LF}} = 10^{-3T_D/T_{60}^{\text{LF}}} = 10^{-3N/f_s T_{60}^{\text{LF}}}$$
$$A_{\text{HF}} = 10^{-3T_D/T_{60}^{\text{HF}}} = 10^{-3N/f_s T_{60}^{\text{HF}}} \tag{8.14}$$

where T_{60}^{LF} and T_{60}^{HF} are the delay times required to reach 60 dB attenuation at low and high frequency, respectively. Thus, given the sample delay N and the 60 dB decay times T_{60}^{LF} and T_{60}^{HF}, we can determine the gain and damping parameters of our damped delay line.

Example 8.2.1. Determine the parameters of a damped delay line to simulate a 100 ms delay with $T_{60}^{\text{LF}} = 3$ s, $T_{60}^{\text{HF}} = 2$ s, and $f_s = 44\,100$ Hz.

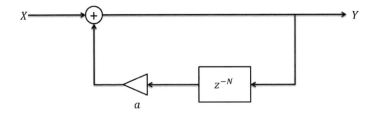

Figure 8.6: Feedback comb filter.

Solution The sample delay is given by $N = f_s T_D = 4410$. We can use Equation (8.14) to determine the low- and high-frequency attenuation.

$$A_{\mathrm{LF}} = 10^{-3N/f_s T_{60}^{\mathrm{LF}}} = 0.7943$$
$$A_{\mathrm{HF}} = 10^{-3N/f_s T_{60}^{\mathrm{HF}}} = 0.7079$$

From these we can determine the damping and gain

$$d = \frac{A_{\mathrm{LF}} - A_{\mathrm{HF}}}{A_{\mathrm{LF}} + A_{\mathrm{HF}}} = 0.0575$$
$$g = \frac{2A_{\mathrm{LF}} A_{\mathrm{HF}}}{A_{\mathrm{LF}} + A_{\mathrm{HF}}} = 0.7487$$

8.2.2   Comb Filters

Comb filters derive their name from the shape of their frequency response plot, which resembles the teeth of a comb. However, their impulse response plot is of greater interest here. Figure 8.6 illustrates a simple feedback comb filter. The output of the filter is the sum of the input and a weighted version of a previous output. The difference equation representation of the feedback comb filter is

$$y(n) = ay(n - N) + x(n) \tag{8.15}$$

and the transfer function is given by

$$H(z) = \frac{1}{1 - az^{-N}} \tag{8.16}$$

A sample impulse response of this filter is shown in Figure 8.7. The response resembles a sequence of echos at regular intervals with exponentially decreasing amplitudes. Echos, or the reflection of sound by walls and other objects in the space, are certainly an element of reverberation, but this impulse response is far too simple and regular to model reverberation.

We can define a more general type of comb filter by replacing a in Equation (8.16) with $A(z)$:

$$H(z) = \frac{1}{1 - A(z)z^{-N}} \tag{8.17}$$

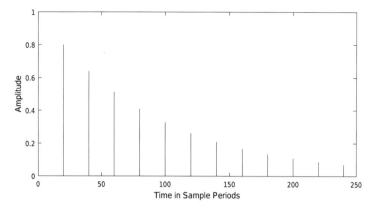

Figure 8.7: Feedback comb filter impulse response ($N = 20$, $a = 0.8$).

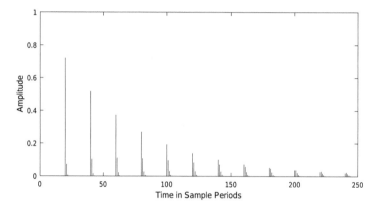

Figure 8.8: Low-pass feedback comb filter impulse response ($N = 20$, $g = 0.8$, $d = 0.1$).

For example, we can use the simple low-pass function Equation (8.11) so that

$$H(z) = \cfrac{1}{1 - \cfrac{g}{1 - dz^{-1}}z^{-N}}$$
$$= \frac{1 - dz^{-1}}{1 - dz^{-1} - gz^{-N}} \qquad (8.18)$$

We call this a low-pass comb filter. The difference equation representation of the low-pass comb filter is

$$y(n) = dy(n - 1) + gy(n - N) + x(n) - dx(n - 1) \qquad (8.19)$$

Figure 8.8 is an example of the impulse response of this filter. The addition of the low-pass feature leads to a richer series of echos.

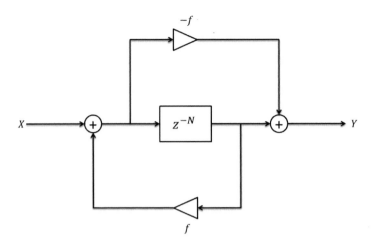

Figure 8.9: A basic all-pass filter.

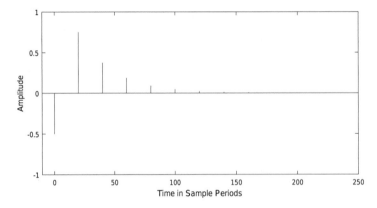

Figure 8.10: Impulse response of a basic all-pass filter ($N = 20$, $f = 0.5$).

8.2.3   All-Pass Filters

The filter shown in Figure 8.9 is an example of an all-pass filter, deriving its name from the fact that the magnitude of its frequency response is unity for all frequencies. The transfer function and difference equation for this filter are given by

$$H(z) = \frac{-f + z^{-N}}{1 - f z^{-N}} \tag{8.20}$$

and

$$y(n) = -f x(n) + x(n - N) + f y(n - N) \tag{8.21}$$

Figure 8.10 shows an example impulse response of this all-pass filter. If we replace the simple delay z^{-N} with an attenuated delay $A(z)z^{-N}$, the result is similar to that obtained with the same change in the comb filter. With this modification, however, the filter is no longer all-pass.

Comb		All-pass
1617	1356	556
1557	1277	441
1491	1188	341
1422	1116	225

Table 8.1: Freeverb filter sample delays (left channel).

8.2.4 Scattering Matrix

Consider an audio element with multiple inputs $x_1(n), \ldots, x_L(n)$ and multiple outputs $y_1(n), \ldots, y_M(n)$ related by

$$\mathbf{y}(n) = \mathbf{S}\mathbf{x}(n) \tag{8.22}$$

where

$$\mathbf{x}(n) = \begin{bmatrix} x_1(n) \\ \vdots \\ x_L(n) \end{bmatrix}$$

$$\mathbf{y}(n) = \begin{bmatrix} y_1(n) \\ \vdots \\ y_M(n) \end{bmatrix} \tag{8.23}$$

and $\mathbf{S}$ is a $M \times L$ matrix that we will refer to as a scattering or mixing matrix. A scattering matrix can model, for example, a multiport audio element where $\mathbf{x}(n)$ and $\mathbf{y}(n)$ are the entering and exiting audio signals [25].

8.3 Schroeder Reverberators

The first *artificial reverberators* were developed in the 1960s by Schroeder and Logan [3]. They used combinations of comb filters, all-pass filters, and mixing matrices to add a reverberation effect to a digital audio signal. They combined comb filters in parallel and all-pass filters in series and sometimes used the mixing matrix to extract one or two output channels from individual filter outputs. A descendant of their work, known as "freeverb," is still widely used. Freeverb was developed by someone known as "Jezar at Dreampoint," and source code for freeverb is currently available at http://blog.bjornroche.com/2012/06/freeverb-original-public-domain-code-by.html and perhaps elsewhere.

The core of freeverb is a cascade of four modified all-pass filters driven by a parallel combination of eight low-pass comb filters. There are two of these 12 filter structures, one for each of two stereo channels. The low-pass comb filters all have the same gain factor g and damping factor d, and the all-pass filters all have the same feedback factor f. The transfer function of the modified all-pass filter is

$$H(z) = \frac{-1 + (1 + f)z^{-N}}{1 - fz^{-N}} \tag{8.24}$$

and $H(z)$ is only all-pass for one particular value of f.

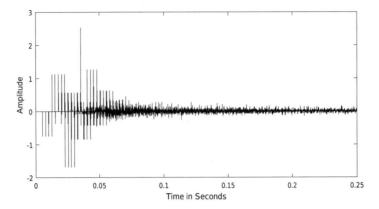

Figure 8.11: Freeverb impulse response ($g = 0.8$, $d = 0.2$, $f = 0.5$).

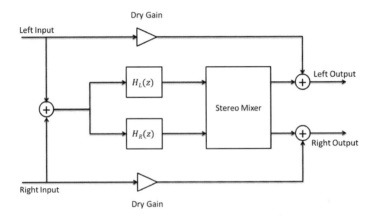

Figure 8.12: Freeverb mixing diagram.

The sample delay values, which Jezar tuned to work well at a sampling rate of 44 100 Hz, are listed in Table 8.1. The table lists the values for the left channel; the values for the right channel are obtained by adding a "stereo spread" value (default 23 samples) to each of the delays listed. The factors g and d are usually made available to the user via a GUI, although the amount of allowed variation is limited in order to avoid stability problems. The value of f is usually fixed at $f = 0.5$. Figure 8.11 shows the impulse response of the left-channel portion of freeverb for nominal parameter values.

Figure 8.12 shows the overall structure of freeverb, which includes a mixing matrix of sorts. As shown in the figure, the left- and right-channel inputs are summed and fed to each of comb/all-pass filter combinations, represented by their overall transfer functions $H_L(z)$ and $H_R(z)$. The outputs of the filter combinations are fed to a stereo mixer along with the original left and right channel inputs (multiplied by a "dry gain" factor). The stereo mixer is a mixing matrix given by

$$\mathbf{S} = \frac{g_W}{2} \begin{bmatrix} 1 + \Delta & 1 - \Delta \\ 1 - \Delta & 1 + \Delta \end{bmatrix} \tag{8.25}$$

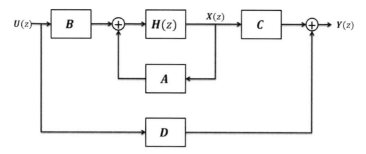

Figure 8.13: State-space model of an LTIS.

where g_W is a "wet gain" factor and Δ is a stereo mix factor ranging from 0 (no separation) to 1 (complete separation).

8.4 State-Space Reverberators

Figure 8.13 shows the z-transform version of a generalized state-space model of an LTIS where the single sample delay z^{-1} has been replaced by a transfer function matrix $\mathbf{H}(z)$. For example, if $\mathbf{H}(z)$ is given by

$$\mathbf{H}(z) = \begin{bmatrix} z^{-M_1} & 0 & \cdots & 0 \\ 0 & z^{-M_2} & \cdots & 0 \\ \vdots & \vdots & \ddots & \vdots \\ 0 & 0 & \cdots & z^{-M_N} \end{bmatrix} \tag{8.26}$$

then each component of the state vector is delayed by a different amount. The resulting system is known as a lossless *feedback delay network* (FDN). We can obtain a more general FDN by adding frequency-dependent attenuation to the delays:

$$\mathbf{H}(z) = \begin{bmatrix} A_1(z)z^{-M_1} & 0 & \cdots & 0 \\ 0 & A_2(z)z^{-M_2} & \cdots & 0 \\ \vdots & \vdots & \ddots & \vdots \\ 0 & 0 & \cdots & A_N(z)z^{-M_N} \end{bmatrix} \tag{8.27}$$

The FDN is the basis for a number of reverberator designs [2, 9]. The input signal is split by the $\mathbf{B}$ matrix, combined with a feedback vector, and applied to parallel damped delay lines with different delays. The outputs of the delay lines are combined via the $\mathbf{C}$ matrix to produce the processed output. The delay line outputs are also fed back via the scattering matrix $\mathbf{A}$. Even without feedback, each sample generates N output samples. With feedback, however, this splitting is repeated so that each input sample eventually contributes a large number of output components.

The design of an FDN reverberator involves choosing the "order" N; the matrices $\mathbf{A}$, $\mathbf{B}$, $\mathbf{C}$, and $\mathbf{D}$; the delays $M_1 \cdots M_N$; and the damping coefficients for each delay line. Since the $\mathbf{D}$ matrix simply controls the mix of the "dry" (unprocessed) and "wet" (processed) signals, we will set it to 0 for now. We will set the $\mathbf{B}$ and $\mathbf{C}$ to a column vector of ones and a row vector of ones, respectively, thus implementing pure split and combine operations. The feedback matrix $\mathbf{A}$ should be a lossless matrix, which will guarantee stability and allow the designer to control the rate of decay by other means. Candidates include the following [9]

- Hadamard matrix: For n equal to a positive power of 2

$$\mathbf{A}_N = \frac{1}{\sqrt{2}} \begin{bmatrix} \mathbf{A}_{N/2} & \mathbf{A}_{N/2} \\ \mathbf{A}_{N/2} & -\mathbf{A}_{N/2} \end{bmatrix} \tag{8.28}$$

where

$$\mathbf{A}_2 = \frac{1}{\sqrt{2}} \begin{bmatrix} 1 & 1 \\ 1 & -1 \end{bmatrix} \tag{8.29}$$

- Householder reflection matrix

$$\mathbf{A}_N = \mathbf{I}_N - \frac{2}{N} \mathbf{O}_N \tag{8.30}$$

where $\mathbf{I}_N$ is the $N \times N$ identity matrix and $\mathbf{O}_N$ is a $N \times N$ matrix of ones.

If we consider the delay lines to represent segments of possible paths taken by acoustic waves in the reverberant space, then we can relate the sample delays to dimensions of the room. For a path segment of length L, the corresponding sample delay is

$$M = f_s L / c \tag{8.31}$$

where c is the speed of sound. Of course it is not practical to identify and measure all of the paths in a space, and we want to limit the value of N to avoid excessive computation. To make things more practical we will determine N path lengths distributed between some minimum and maximum length. For example, we can start with some maximum path length $L_{\max}$, choose a minimum path length $L_{\min}$ (e.g., $L_{\min} = L_{\max}/N$), and calculate an exponential sequence of lengths from $L_{\min}$ to $L_{\max}$. These lengths can then be used to determine the sample delays.

The impulse response of an FDN includes thousands of echoes of the original impulse, each delayed by some combination of the chosen sample delays. It is desirable to avoid having many of these combinations result in the same delay. This can be accomplished by adjusting each sample delay to a nearby prime number.

Given the sample delays and desired decay times, we can use the procedure from Section 8.2.1 to complete the design of the damped delay lines.

Example 8.4.1. In this example, we will illustrate the design of an FDN reverberator.

We start with the following design decisions:

- The "order" of the system is $N = 8$ (The actual order of the FDN is much greater than N).

- The feedback matrix is given by Equation (8.30). The matrix then turns out to be

$$\mathbf{A} = \begin{bmatrix} -0.75 & 0.25 & \cdots & 0.25 \\ 0.25 & -0.75 & \cdots & 0.25 \\ \vdots & \vdots & \ddots & \vdots \\ 0.25 & 0.25 & \cdots & -0.75 \end{bmatrix}$$

Index	Sample Delay
1	3853
2	2861
3	2113
4	1579
5	1171
6	863
7	647
8	479

Table 8.2: Sample delays for example FDN.

- The **B** and **C** matrices are given by

$$\mathbf{B} = \frac{1}{\sqrt{N}} \begin{bmatrix} 1 \\ 1 \\ \vdots \\ 1 \end{bmatrix}$$

and

$$\mathbf{C} = \begin{bmatrix} 1 & 1 & \cdots & 1 \end{bmatrix}$$

We will now determine the sample delays M_n based on an assumed maximum path length $L_{\max}$. The maximum sample delay is then

$$M_{\max} = f_s L_{\max}/c$$

where f_s is the sampling rate and c is the speed of sound in units consistent with those of $L_{\max}$. We will set the minimum sample delay to $M_{\min} = M_{\max}/N$. We then calculate a roughly exponential sequence of delays according to

$$\hat{M}_n = \text{round}(\alpha^{n-1} M_{\max})$$

where

$$\alpha = \left(\frac{M_{\min}}{M_{\max}} \right)^{\frac{1}{N-1}}$$

Finally, we adjust $\hat{M}_n$ to a nearby prime number to determine the final sample delays M_n. Table 8.2 lists sample delays determined by this method for $L_{\max} = 30$ m and $c = 343.2$ m/s.

Once we have the sample delays, we can determine the damping and gain coefficients for the delay lines using the procedure described in Section 8.2.1. The resulting coefficients for $T_{60}^{\text{LF}} = 3$ s and $T_{60}^{\text{HF}} = 2$ s are listed in Table 8.3.

Figure 8.14 is a plot of the impulse response of the FDN reverberator.

8.5 Reverberators Using Multiport Elements

A reverberator structure similar to the FDN can be developed on the basis of multiport acoustic elements as described in [25] and [19]. A multiport acoustic

Index	Damping	Gain
1	0.050252	0.776674
2	0.037328	0.829093
3	0.027574	0.870848
4	0.020608	0.901886
5	0.015284	0.926313
6	0.011264	0.945172
7	0.008445	0.958618
8	0.006252	0.969202

Table 8.3: Damping and gain coefficients for example FDN.

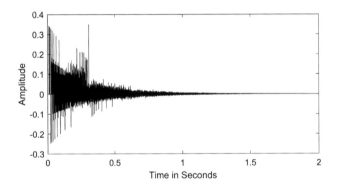

Figure 8.14: Impulse response of an FDN reverberator.

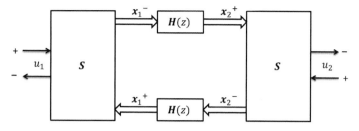

Figure 8.15: Network of multiport elements.

element is defined by the relation

$$\mathbf{x}^- = \mathbf{S}\mathbf{x}^+ \tag{8.32}$$

where $\mathbf{x}^+$ is a vector of acoustic inputs, $\mathbf{x}^-$ is a vector of acoustic outputs, and $\mathbf{S}$ is a matrix defining their relationship. In the context of a digital reverberator, the acoustic inputs and outputs are sequences of samples, and the z-transform version of Equation (8.32) becomes

$$\mathbf{x}^-(z) = \mathbf{S}(z)\mathbf{x}^+(z) \tag{8.33}$$

Figure 8.15 shows a multiport element network (MPN) with inputs denoted by arrows entering the elements and outputs by arrows leaving the elements. There are two types of elements: a delay element with matrix $\mathbf{H}(z)$ given by Equation (8.27) and a reflection matrix $\mathbf{S}$ similar to the Householder matrix Equation (8.30). The external inputs and outputs are scalar pairs denoted u_1 and u_2, and internal inputs and outputs are vector pairs denoted $\mathbf{x}_1$ and $\mathbf{x}_2$. The reflection matrix $\mathbf{S}$ is partitioned as follows:

$$\mathbf{S} = \begin{bmatrix} \mathbf{A} & \mathbf{B} \\ \mathbf{C} & 0 \end{bmatrix} \tag{8.34}$$

The input/output relationship for the reflection element is therefore

$$\mathbf{x}_k^-(z) = \mathbf{A}\mathbf{x}_k^+(z) + \mathbf{B}u_k^+(z)$$
$$u_k^-(z) = \mathbf{C}\mathbf{x}_k^+(z) \tag{8.35}$$

The internal inputs are also related by the delay elements:

$$\mathbf{x}_2^+(z) = \mathbf{H}(z)\mathbf{x}_1^-$$
$$\mathbf{x}_1^+(z) = \mathbf{H}(z)\mathbf{x}_2^- \tag{8.36}$$

Figure 8.16 is an expanded view of the MPN.

The system shown in Figure 8.16 looks like a combination of two FDNs, especially if the matrices $\mathbf{A}$, $\mathbf{B}$, $\mathbf{C}$, and $\mathbf{H}(z)$ are defined as they were for the FDN. As we will show in the example, the impulse response of the system matches the criteria for producing a reverberation effect. Moreover, it fits well with two-channel (stereo) audio with inputs u_1^+ and u_2^+ and outputs u_1^- and u_2^-.

Example 8.5.1. We can create an example of the MPN reverberator using the same matrices as in Example 8.4.1. The resulting impulse response is shown in Figure 8.17.

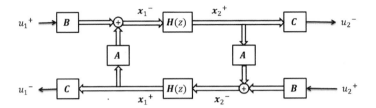

Figure 8.16: Expanded multiport element network.

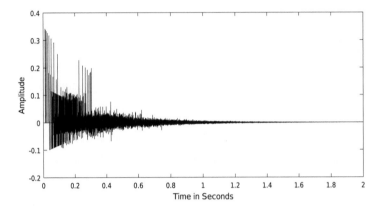

Figure 8.17: MPN reverberator impulse response.

8.6   Summary

This chapter has introduced a number of methods for adding a reverberation effect to an audio signal, all based on a digital LTIS characterized by an impulse response. We have shown both how to measure the impulse response of a physical space and how to design a digital LTIS that has a reverberant impulse response.

Chapter 9

Audio Compression

The development of the audio CD led to, among other things, a de facto standard for audio quality. People often use the phrase "CD quality audio" as a benchmark for measuring audio quality. Earlier the phrase "high fidelity" was applied to audio recordings that were deemed to be of high quality. Oddly, although there were a few proposals, there was no generally accepted standard for what constituted high fidelity. The CD format (i.e., 16-bit PCM with a sampling frequency of 44.1 kHz), on the other hand, is an industry standard based on both engineering principles and listener evaluation.

In the 1990s the CD format came up against the existing limits of data storage and transmission. For example, 3 min of stereo audio at 44 100 samples/s and 16 bits/sample requires more than 30 MB of storage and would have required more than 3 h to download at the modem speeds of the time. Thus, there was considerable motivation to find ways to reduce the amount of audio data without sacrificing audio quality. Of course the same motivation existed in the telecommunications industry due to the growth of both voice and other data communication. But the audio quality required for voice communication is considerably less than for music.

In Section 6.6 we discussed an audio *source model* based on linear predictive coding that can be used to reduce the amount of data needed to store or transmit high-quality audio. In this chapter we will consider audio compression based on a *listener model*. Specifically, this chapter presents an overview of an approach to audio compression generally known as *MPEG audio*. MPEG audio makes use of our knowledge of human auditory perception to reduce the amount of data needed to record audio. MPEG audio is an example of *lossy compression*, in that we cannot exactly recover the original audio signal from the MPEG audio stream. Nevertheless, to many ears the sound produced by MPEG audio is quite acceptable. A complete description of MPEG audio is contained in [29] and useful summaries can be found in [36] and [28]. We will limit our coverage to the most basic form of MPEG audio: MPEG level 1.

As usual, we begin with a digital audio signal $x(n)$ with an associated sampling rate f_s. To create MPEG audio we have to perform two parallel processes on the signal. In one branch we pass the signal through an analysis filter that divides the audio spectrum into M equal-width subbands. The sampling rate of the subband signals is reduced to f_s/M. In the other branch we apply the *psychoacoustic model*

147

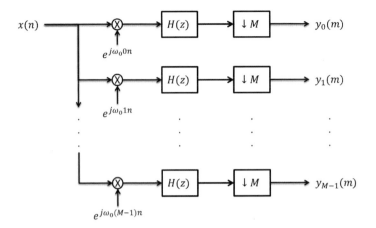

Figure 9.1: Analysis filter bank.

of human hearing that ultimately determines a *masking threshold* for each subband. The two branches merge in a process to encode the subband samples based on a comparison of the subband signal level and the associated masking threshold. Whereas the input samples are typically coded using 16 or more bits/sample, significantly fewer bits may be required to code the subband samples. In fact, some subband samples may be simply ignored. This is how MPEG audio achieves compression.

9.1   Polyphase Analysis and Synthesis Filters

The filter bank requirements for MPEG are straightforward: the analysis filter bank should divide the audio spectrum equally into M subbands. In this section we will describe the polyphase filter bank that is the basis of the MPEG audio analysis filter. We will also describe the corresponding synthesis filter that can reconstruct the original signal from the subband signals.

9.1.1   Analysis Filter

Figure 9.1 illustrates a filter bank with a single input $x(n)$ and M outputs $y_k(m)$. The kth output is obtained from $x(n)$ by (1) shifting the frequency spectrum by $\omega_0 k$ radians/sample ($\omega_0 = 2\pi/M$), (2) low-pass filtering through $H(z)$, and (3) downsampling the shifted/filtered signal by M samples. Thus, the output is a set of M low-pass signals derived from each of M equal-width segments of the audio spectrum. Such a filter bank is straightforward to implement, but not very efficient. For example, the downsampling ignores most of output of the low-pass filters. Fortunately, we can derive a much more efficient structure that is exactly equivalent.

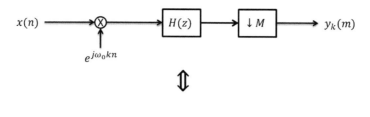

Figure 9.2: Analysis subfilter equivalence.

We begin by determining the output $v_k(n)$ of the kth low-pass filter.

$$v_k(n) = \sum_{i=0}^{N-1} h(i)e^{j\omega_0 k(n-i)}x(n-i)$$

$$= e^{j\omega_0 kn} \sum_{i=0}^{N-1} h(i)e^{-j\omega_0 ki}x(n-i)$$

$$= e^{j\omega_0 kn} \sum_{i=0}^{N-1} h_k(i)x(n-i) \quad (9.1)$$

where N is the order of the low-pass filter, which is assumed to be a FIR filter. Since $e^{j\omega_0 kn} = 1$ if n is an integer multiple of M, this term will not affect the downsampled output and can be ignored. We are now obtaining $v_k(n)$ as the output of a shifted filter $h_k(n)$. Figure 9.2 shows the equivalence relation. Next we determine and manipulate the z-transform of $h_k(n)$:

$$H_k(z) = \sum_{n=-\infty}^{\infty} h_k(n)z^{-n}$$

$$= \sum_{l=0}^{M-1} \sum_{n=-\infty}^{\infty} h_k(nM+l)z^{-(nM+l)}$$

$$= \sum_{l=0}^{M-1} \sum_{n=-\infty}^{\infty} h(nM+l)e^{-j\omega_0 k(nM+l)}z^{-(nM+l)}$$

$$= \sum_{l=0}^{M-1} e^{-j\omega_0 kl}z^{-l} \sum_{n=-\infty}^{\infty} h(nM+l)z^{-nM}$$

$$= \sum_{l=0}^{M-1} e^{-j\omega_0 kl}z^{-l}P_l(z^M) \quad (9.2)$$

where

$$p_l(n) = h(nM+l) \quad (9.3)$$

and $P_l(z)$ is the z-transform of $p_l(n)$. Figure 9.3 illustrates the structure of the kth subband filter using Equation (9.2). We have taken advantage of the fact that we

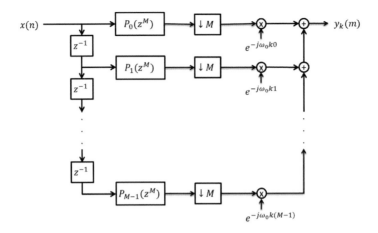

Figure 9.3: Analysis subfilter 1.

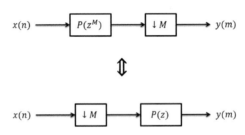

Figure 9.4: Noble identity 1.

can reverse the order of downsampling and both summation and multiplication by a constant.

Figure 9.4 illustrates one of the *noble identities* [41], which allows us to interchange the order of downsampling and filtering. Figure 9.5 shows the result of applying this identity to our filter. Note that the left-hand part of the filter is independent of the subband index k. Moreover, we can see that $y_k(m)$ is a component of the DFT of the outputs of the filters $P_l(z)$. Thus, the complete analysis filter bank can be realized as shown in Figure 9.6. This realization is far more efficient than the one shown in Figure 9.1.

Now let us consider how we might implement our improved filter bank. We start by assuming that the original low-pass filter $H(z)$ is a FIR filter of order N and that $N = ML$ for some integer L. Thus, the coefficients of subfilter $P_l(z)$ are $h(l), h(M + l), \ldots, h[(L - 1)M + l]$ (note that $P_l(z)$ is a FIR filter of order L). If the sample time n is an integer multiple of M then sample $x(n - l)$ arrives at the input of subfilter l. The most recent L samples to arrive at the input to subfilter l are $x(n-l), x[n - (M + l)], \ldots, x\{n - [(L - 1)M + l]\}$. Thus, the output of subfilter l is

$$v_l(m) = \sum_{i=0}^{L-1} h(iM + l)x[n - (iM + l)] \tag{9.4}$$

where $m = n/M$. Now consider the set of N products of the form $h(i)x(n - i)$.

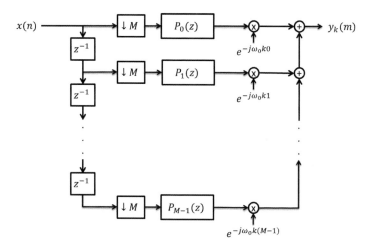

Figure 9.5: Analysis subfilter 2.

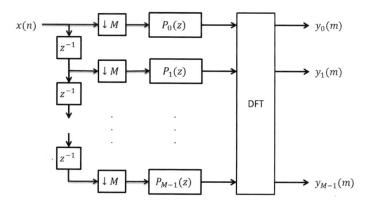

Figure 9.6: Final structure of analysis filter bank.

Each subfilter output is the sum of a subset of those products. The products are evaluated and summed every M samples. This leads to the following procedure, which we describe with the help of MATLAB statements.

First we define some constants:

```
N=1024;
M=32;
L=N/M;
```

Next we compute the filter coefficients and initialize a buffer to contain the N most recent samples:

```
h=fir1 (N−1,1/M);
b=zeros (1,N);
```

The MATLAB function `fir1` as used above calculates the coefficients of the desired low-pass filter. Next we set up an audio-file reader to read in blocks of M samples:

```
AFR=dsp.AudioFileReader ('Same_Old_Lines.wav' ,...
    'SamplesPerFrame' ,M);
```

Finally, we set up a loop that processes the sample blocks to produce the filter bank outputs:

```
while ˜isDone (AFR)
    x=step (AFR);
    b=[fliplr (x')  b (1:end−M)];
    w=h.∗b;
    v=sum(reshape(w,[M L]) ,2);
    y=fft (v);
end
```

For each iteration of the loop we do the following:

- Use the `step` method to get the next M samples from the audio-file reader.

- Shift the M samples into the buffer, making sure that the most recent sample is last.

- Compute the N products.

- Compute the subfilter outputs as the sums of the appropriate subsets of the products. The MATLAB `sum` and `reshape` functions are very handy here.

- Compute the filter bank outputs as the DFT of the subfilter outputs.

9.1.2   Interpolation Filter

Figure 9.7 shows the initial form of the interpolation filter that reconstructs $x(n)$ from the subband components $y_k(m)$. The upsampling function $\uparrow M$ increases the sampling rate by M by inserting $M - 1$ zeros after each sample of $y_k(m)$. The low-pass filter $H(z)$ provides interpolation and the interpolated signal is shifted to its original frequency band. Again we want to modify this straightforward but inefficient structure.

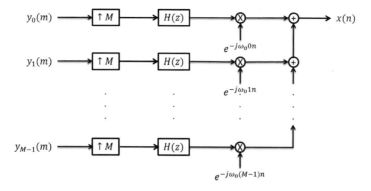

Figure 9.7: Interpolation filter bank.

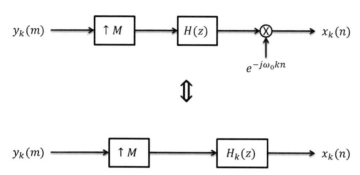

Figure 9.8: Interpolation subfilter equivalence.

Let $x_k(n)$ be the component of $x(n)$ derived from $y_k(m)$ and let $v_k(n)$ and $u_k(n)$ be the output of the corresponding low-pass filter and upsampler. Then

$$x_k(n) = e^{-j\omega_0 kn} v_k(n)$$

$$= e^{-j\omega_0 kn} \sum_{i=0}^{N-1} h(i) u_k(n-i)$$

$$= \sum_{i=0}^{N-1} h(i) e^{-j\omega_0 ki} u_k(n-i) e^{-j\omega_0 k(n-i)}$$

$$= \sum_{i=0}^{N-1} h_k(i) u_k(n-i) e^{-j\omega_0 k(n-i)} \tag{9.5}$$

Note that the shifted filter $H_k(z)$ appears once again, this time acting on the input $u_k(n) e^{j\omega_0 kn}$. However, $u(n)$ is nonzero only if n is an integer multiple of M, and therefore the exponential term can again be ignored. This leads to the equivalence relation shown in Figure 9.8.

Figure 9.9 illustrates the expanded version of the kth interpolation subfilter. The expansion of $H_k(z)$ differs from the one shown in Figure 9.3, but is equivalent. We have again moved the upsampling operation to a more convenient location without changing its effect. Figure 9.10 shows the second noble identity, which allows us to

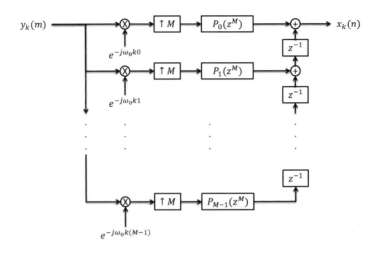

Figure 9.9: Interpolation subfilter 1.

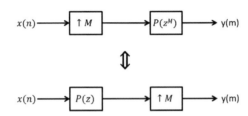

Figure 9.10: Noble identity 2.

convert the subfilter to the form shown in Figure 9.11. Putting all of the subfilters together, we arrive at the final structure shown in Figure 9.12.

9.1.3   MPEG Layer 1 Implementation

Somewhat modified versions of the analysis and synthesis filters derived in this section are used in practice. The MPEG layer 1 analysis filter uses the modified discrete cosine transform (MDCT) instead of the DFT. The prototype low-pass filter has order $N = 512$, and the coefficients are defined in the standard. Although the analysis filter still provides $M = 32$ subbands, there are $2M = 64$ inputs to the MDCT.

The MDCT as defined in the standard is given by

$$y_k(m) = \sum_{i=0}^{2M-1} \cos\left[\frac{\pi}{2M}(2i+1)(n-M/2)\right] v_i(m) \tag{9.6}$$

where the $v_i(m)$ values are computed after every M^{th} input sample from the most recent N input samples as follows:

$$v_i(m) = \sum_{j=0}^{\frac{N}{2M}-1} w(i+2Mj) \tag{9.7}$$

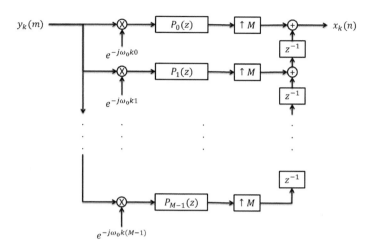

Figure 9.11: Interpolation subfilter 2.

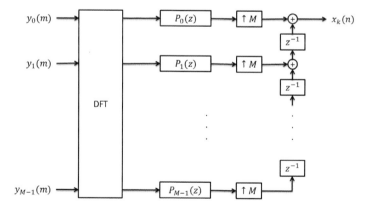

Figure 9.12: Final structure of interpolation filter.

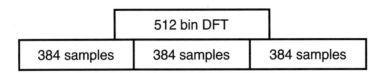

Figure 9.13: Short-term DFT analysys in MPEG-1 model 1.

where $w(j)$ is a vector of the most recent N samples weighted by the filter coefficients $h(j)$. The interpolation filter is modified in a similar manner.

9.2 Psychoacoustic Model

Although the analysis and synthesis filters are important components of an MPEG audio system, they do not provide any of the compression. For example, if the input to the analysis filter has a sampling rate of 44 100 Hz then the output is 32 parallel subband channels with rates of 1378.125 Hz. If the bit depth (i.e., the number of bits per sample) is unchanged, then there is no compression. In MPEG, however, the bit depths of the subband channels are varied dynamically according to the psychoacoustic model.

The psychoacoustic model is based on our knowledge of the human auditory system and how people perceive sound. For example, we do not hear as well at all frequencies. In addition, there are masking effects that prevent us from hearing one sound in the presence of another. The psychoacoustic model provides time- and frequency-dependent thresholds that can be used to dynamically allocate coding bits to the subband signals. The basic approach is as follows:

- Calculate the sound pressure level in each subband.

- Calculate the minimum audible sound pressure level in each band. This minimum is determined by the threshold of human hearing and masking effects.

These values are computed periodically based on blocks of input samples and are used to allocate coding bits to the subband signals.

In the rest of this section, we will describe in more detail psychoacoustic model 1, layer 1 as defined in the ISO/IEC standard for MPEG [29].

9.2.1 Sound Pressure Level Analysis

Although the analysis filter breaks the audio signal into a set of frequency subbands, the psychoacoustic model includes its own spectral analysis based on straightforward application of the DFT. Specifically, model 1 computes an $N = 512$ bin power spectrum centered on blocks of 384 input samples as shown in Figure 9.13 so that each calculation includes 64 samples from each adjacent block. Each block of 384 input samples corresponds to 32 blocks of 12 analysis filter output samples. The power spectrum $\mathbf{P}$ is given by

$$\mathbf{P} = 20\log_{10}\left[|\text{DFT}(\mathbf{w} \cdot \mathbf{x})|/N\right] \tag{9.8}$$

where $\mathbf{x}$ is a vector of N input samples, $\mathbf{w}$ is a Hann window given by

$$w(n) = 0.5\sqrt{8/3}(1 - \cos 2\pi n/N) \tag{9.9}$$

and $\mathbf{w} \cdot \mathbf{x}$ is a vector of the products of the elements of $\mathbf{w}$ and $\mathbf{x}$. An offset is then added to the power spectrum so that it has a maximum value of 96 dB SPL.

The sound pressure level in a subband is taken to be the maximum of two values. The first value is calculated from the power spectrum as follows:

$$P_1(k) = \max_{n \in \mathcal{B}(k)} P(n) \tag{9.10}$$

where $\mathcal{B}(k)$ is the range of frequency bins corresponding to subband k. The second value is derived from the subband filter output samples $y_k(m)$. We first calculate $y_k^{\max}$ as

$$y_k^{\max} = \max_m(|y_k(m)|) \tag{9.11}$$

where the range of m covers the block of 12 output samples. Next we quantize this value using a 64-level (6-bit) nonlinear quantizing algorithm based on *scale factors*. The 64 scale factors are given by

$$F_i = 2\alpha^i \tag{9.12}$$

for $i = 0, 1, \ldots, 63$ where $\alpha = 0.5^{1/3}$. The scale factor for $y_k^{\max}$ is the smallest F_i such that $F_i > y_k^{\max}$. This scale factor $F_{\min}^k$ determines the second sound pressure level value as follows:

$$P_2(k) = 20 \log_{10} 2^{15} F_{\min}^k - 10 \tag{9.13}$$

The sound pressure level of subband k, $P_T(k)$, is the maximum of $P_1(k)$ and $P_2(k)$, i.e.,

$$P_T(k) = \max[P_1(k), P_2(k)] \tag{9.14}$$

To get a better understanding of Equation (9.13), consider the sound pressure level associated with the ith scale factor.

$$\begin{aligned}
P_i &= 20 \log_{10} 2^{15} F_i - 10 \\
&= 20 \log_{10} 2^{16} \alpha^i - 10 \\
&= 320 \log_{10} 2 + 20 \log_{10} 0.5^{i/3} - 10 \\
&= 96.3296 - 2.0069i - 10 \tag{9.15}
\end{aligned}$$

Thus, the scale factors restrict $P_2(k)$ to one of a set of 64 discrete values decreasing in steps of about 2 dB SPL from a maximum of about 86 dB SPL. According to the standard, the 10 dB SPL adjustment "corrects for the difference between peak and RMS level" [29].

The key to coding the subband samples is the difference between the sound pressure level in the subband and a threshold based on the threshold of human hearing and thresholds based on masking.

9.2.2 Threshold of Hearing

Each subband sound pressure level must exceed a subband threshold in order to be audible. The most basic threshold is the threshold of human hearing.

In Chapter 2 we noted that an acoustic pressure of 0 dB SPL corresponds to the threshold of human hearing, i.e., the weakest sound that a healthy young person

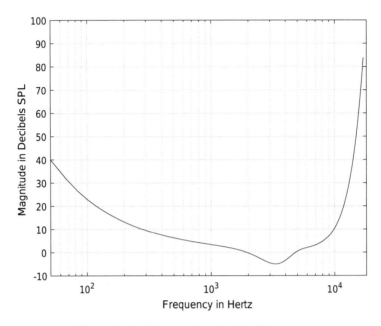

Figure 9.14: Human threshold of hearing.

can hear. It turns out, however, that our ability to hear is frequency-dependent, and 0 dB SPL sound is only audible around a sweet spot in the audio spectrum. The following empirical formula approximates the threshold of hearing for a healthy young person as a function of frequency [28]:

$$\Theta(f) = 3.64 f^{-0.8} - 6.5 e^{-0.6(f-3.3)^2} - 10^{-3} f^4 \tag{9.16}$$

where $\Theta(f)$ is the threshold in dB SPL and f is the frequency in kilohertz. Figure 9.14 is a plot of Equation (9.16). The minimum threshold of hearing is about -5 dB SPL at about 3300 Hz. At 50 Hz, however, the threshold increases to 40 dB SPL, and at 17 kHz the threshold is more than 70 dB SPL. Table 9.1 lists the minimum threshold of hearing for each of the 32 analysis filter bands.

9.2.3   Frequency Masking

Suppose a sound consists of a pure tone with a certain frequency and magnitude. If you add a second tone at a nearby frequency with a lower magnitude, that tone may be inaudible, even if its magnitude is greater than the threshold of hearing for that frequency. This effect is known as *tonal masking* and is one example of frequency masking: the ability of a sound at one frequency to mask a simultaneous sound at another frequency. We can quantify this effect as a masking threshold, as roughly sketched in Figure 9.15. The dashed curve indicates the masking threshold associated with the tonal sound. Other frequency components of the sound must exceed this threshold to be audible. Nontonal audio also creates a masking effect. We will now look at how frequency masking effects are quantified in model 1, layer 1 [29].

Band	dB SPL	Band	dB SPL
1	5	2	2
3	−1	4	−4
5	−5	6	−5
7	−3	8	0
9	2	10	2
11	3	12	4
13	5	14	7
15	9	16	12
17	15	18	19
19	24	20	30
21	37	22	44
23	53	24	63
25	75	26	88
27	103	28	120
29	139	30	160
31	183	32	209

Table 9.1: Minimum threshold of hearing by frequency band.

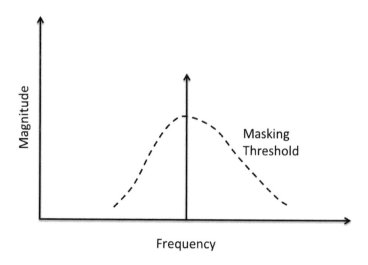

Figure 9.15: Tonal masking threshold.

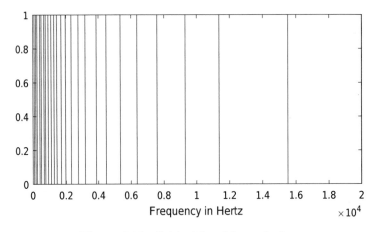

Figure 9.16: Critical band boundaries.

The first step is to locate the tonal and nontonal components that contribute to the masking thresholds. These components are determined from the power spectrum **P** from Equation (9.8). To find tonal components, we start by finding the local maxima, i.e., components of the power spectrum that satisfy

$$P(n) > P(n-1)$$
$$P(n) \geq P(n+1) \tag{9.17}$$

Tonal components are local maxima that satisfy a more rigorous condition. In model 1, layer 1 the condition is

$$P(n) - P(n+j) \geq 7\,\mathrm{dB} \quad \forall j \in J \tag{9.18}$$

where

$$J = \begin{cases} \{-2, +2\} & 2 < n < 63 \\ \{-3, -2, +2, +3\} & 64 \leq n < 127 \\ \{-6, \ldots, -2, +2, \ldots, +6\} & 127 \leq n \leq 250 \end{cases} \tag{9.19}$$

The kth tonal component is associated with its frequency bin index n_k and a power level given by

$$T(k) = 10\log_{10}\left[10^{P(n_k-1)/10} + 10^{P(n_k)/10} + 10^{P(n_k+1)/10}\right] \tag{9.20}$$

Frequency bins in $J \cup \{-1, +1\}$ are flagged so that they will not be considered in subsequent analysis (e.g., set $P(n) = -\infty\,\mathrm{dB}$ for $n \in J \cup \{-1, +1\}$).

Nontonal components are derived from the remaining frequency components (i.e., neither tonal components nor neighbors of tonal components). In order to determine the nontonal components, we need to introduce *critical bands*, a set of 25 nonuniform frequency bands covering the audio spectrum as shown in Figure 9.16. These bands model segments of the cochlea in the inner ear that respond to different frequency bands and are tabulated in [29]. Each critical band contributes one nontonal component. The power of a nontonal component is the sum of the powers of remaining frequency components in the band, and the frequency index of the component is based on the geometric mean of the frequencies in the band. We will let $U(k)$ and m_k be the power and frequency bin index, respectively, of the kth nontonal component.

The *Bark* frequency scale is based on the critical bands. The Bark frequency $z(f)$ corresponding to frequency f (in hertz) is given by the following empirical formula [28]:

$$z(f) = 13\arctan(0.00076f) + 3.5\arctan\left[\left(\frac{f}{7500}\right)^2\right] \quad (9.21)$$

Frequency masking thresholds are based on the Bark frequency scale. However, before we calculate masking thresholds, we can seek to eliminate some of the tonal and nontonal components.

First of all, we can eliminate any tonal or nontonal component with power less than the threshold of hearing at the associated frequency. Second, we remove from consideration any tonal component that is within a frequency distance of 0.5 Bark from a more powerful tonal component, which would render the less powerful component inaudible.

In addition to reducing the numbers of masking components, we also reduce the frequency resolution from 256 bins to a smaller number. For model 1, layer 1 with a sampling frequency of 44 100 Hz, the 256 DFT frequency bins are mapped into 106 frequency bins. The first 48 bins in the reduced set are the corresponding DFT bins. DFT bins 49–96, however, are mapped into one half as many bins, and DFT bins 97–232 are mapped into one quarter as many bins. The frequencies associated with the reduced set of bins are the highest associated DFT bin frequency. DFT bins 233–256 are also mapped to the last bin of the reduced set, but the frequency is taken from DFT bin 232. Each of the reduced bins has an associated critical band and Bark frequency. Table D.1b in [29] lists the details.

As a result of the frequency bin reduction, each remaining masking component receives a new index $i \in \{1, 2, \ldots, 106\}$ with corresponding Bark frequency z_i. Each masking component has an associated masking threshold function $M_i(z)$. For tonal components, the masking threshold is given by [28]

$$M_i^T(z) = T(i) - 0.275z_i + S_i(z - z_i) - 6.025 \quad (9.22)$$

where

$$S_i(x) = \begin{cases} 17x - 0.4T(i) + 11 & -3 \le x < -1 \\ (0.4T(i) + 6)x & -1 \le x < 0 \\ -17x & 0 \le x < 1 \\ (0.15T(i) - 17)x - 0.15T_i & 1 \le x < 8 \end{cases} \quad (9.23)$$

The masking threshold is undefined outside the range indicated in Equation (9.23). Figure 9.17 is a plot of the tonal masking threshold function for $T(i) = 60$ dB and $z_i = 10$ Bark. The masking threshold for a nontonal component is given by a similar equation:

$$M_i^U(z) = U(i) - 0.175z_i + S_i(z - z_i) - 2.025 \quad (9.24)$$

where $S_i(x)$ is given by Equation (9.23) with $T(i)$ replaced by $U(i)$.

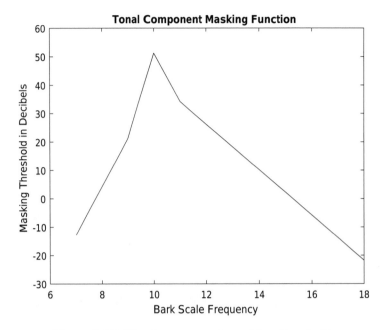

Figure 9.17: Tonal component masking threshold.

9.2.4   Global Masking Threshold and Signal-to-Mask Ratio

In this section we will determine an overall threshold based on both the threshold of hearing and frequency masking and map this threshold to our original subbands. We will then discuss the relation between this global threshold and the subband signal power.

The *global masking threshold* is the power sum of the threshold of hearing and the two masking functions as follows:

$$G(i) = 10 \log_{10} \left[10^{0.1\Theta(z_i)} + \sum_{j=1}^{N_T} 10^{0.1 M_j^T(z_i)} + \sum_{j=1}^{N_U} 10^{0.1 M_j^U(z_i)} \right] \qquad (9.25)$$

where $i = 1, 2, \ldots, 106$, $\Theta(z)$ is the threshold of hearing at Bark frequency z, and N_T and N_U are the numbers of tonal and nontonal masking components, respectively.

Now we return our attention to the subbands corresponding to the analysis and synthesis filter banks developed in Section 9.1. The masking threshold for the kth subband is given by

$$G^{SB}(k) = \min_{i \in \mathcal{B}(k)} G(i) \qquad (9.26)$$

where $\mathcal{B}(k)$ is now the subset of reduced bins corresponding to subband k. The signal-to-mask ratio in subband k can now be determined as

$$\text{SMR}(k) = P_T(k) - G^{\text{SB}}(k) \qquad (9.27)$$

9.3 Subband Sample Coding

In this section we present a brief overview of the process for coding subband samples. Our main objective is to show how the output of the psychoacoustic model affects the coding.

As described in [29], MPEG audio is specified to achieve one of a given set of bit rates. Thus, for a given frame of subband samples, there are a certain number of bits available to be distributed among the samples. In MPEG layer 1, each frame consists of 12 consecutive samples from each subband. The coding process is based on the subband mask-to-noise ratios defined as

$$\text{MNR}(k) = \text{SNR}(k) - \text{SMR}(k) \tag{9.28}$$

where $\text{SNR}(k)$ is the subband signal-to-noise ratio, which can be increased by allocating more bits to the subband. Specifically, [29] states the following criterion: "Minimize the total noise-to-mask ratio over the frame with the constraint that the number of bits used does not exceed the number of bits available for that frame." This criterion is achieved by an iterative bit allocation procedure.

The signal-to-noise ratio as a function of the number of signal levels is tabulated in [29]. Since the number of signal levels is related to the number of bits/sample, the SNR could also be tabulated according to this number. In this case, the values closely match the following simple formula:

$$SNR = 2 + 6B \tag{9.29}$$

where B is the number of bits/sample. Thus, each bit adds 6 dB to the SNR, which is the result we obtained in Section 3.3.1.

9.4 Summary

This section provides some information about one of the many audio compression standards that are in use at the current time. Several more recent formats are now available, some of which are advertised as "lossless," and audio players usually support multiple formats. Many of these formats are based on models of the human listener that reflect both the preferences and limitations of the listener. We saw earlier (Chapter 6) that we can achieve compression based on audio source models as well. Both approaches are part of ongoing research and development.

Note, however, that during the time that audio compression has been perfected, the constraints that drove its development have been relaxed. Download speeds and storage capacities are much greater than they were during the 1990s. Nevertheless, some variant of MPEG remains the preferred format for commercial music sources, perhaps driven by the desire to carry hours of entertainment in your shirt pocket.

Bibliography

[1] J. W. Cooley and J. W. Tukey, "An algorithm for the machine calculation of complex Fourier series," *Mathematics of Computation*, vol. 19, no. 90, pp. 297–301, Apr. 1965.

[2] J.-M. Jot and A. Chaigne, "Digital delay networks for designing artificial reverberators," in *Audio Engineering Society Convention 90*. Audio Engineering Society, 1991.

[3] M. R. Schroeder and B. F. Logan, "Colorless artificial reverberation," *IRE Transactions on Audio*, no. 6, pp. 209–214, 1961.

[4] M. Vorländer, *Auralization: Fundamentals of Acoustics, Modelling, Simulation, Algorithms and Acoustic Virtual Reality*. Berlin: Springer, 2007.

[5] F. J. Fahy, *Foundations of Engineering Acoustics*. Burlington, MA, USA: Academic Press, 2000.

[6] B. Lathi, *Signal Processing and Linear Systems*. New York, NY, USA: Oxford University Press, 1998.

[7] J. O. Smith, *Mathematics of the Discrete Fourier Transform (DFT): With Audio Applications*. Julius Smith, 2007.

[8] ——, *Introduction to Digital Filters: With Audio Applications*. Julius Smith, 2008, vol. 2.

[9] ——, *Physical Audio Signal Processing: For Virtual Musical Instruments and Digital Audio Effects*. Julius Smith, 2006.

[10] ——, *Spectral Audio Signal Processing*. Julius Smith, 2011.

[11] *MATLAB version 8.0.0 (R2012b)*. Natick, MA, USA: MathWorks, 2012.

[12] F. van Saane, "Impulse responses," September 2004, accessed September 9, 2012. [Online]. Available: http://fokkie.home.xs4all.nl/IR.htm.

[13] L. P. Calba and M. L. R. de Campos, "Butterworth filters," in *Wiley Encyclopedia of Electrical and Electronics Engineering*. New York, NY, USA: Wiley-Interscience, 1999, vol. 1, pp. 657–661.

[14] D. Pan, "A tutorial on mpeg/audio compression," *IEEE Multimedia magazine*, vol. 2, no. 2, pp. 60–74, 1995.

164

[15] D. B. Williams and V. Madisetti, *Digital Signal Processing Handbook*. Boca Raton, FL, USA: CRC Press, 1997.

[16] A. Farina, "Simultaneous measurement of impulse response and distortion with a swept-sine technique," in *Audio Engineering Society Convention 108*. Audio Engineering Society, 2000, pp. 18–22.

[17] A. Novák, L. Simon, F. Kadlec, and P. Lotton, "Nonlinear system identification using exponential swept-sine signal," *IEEE Trans. on Instrum. Meas.*, vol. 59, no. 8, pp. 2220–2229, 2010.

[18] R. Stewart and M. Sandler, "Database of omnidirectional and B-format room impulse responses," in *IEEE Int. Conf. on Acoustics Speech and Signal Processing*, March 2010, pp. 165–168.

[19] W. L. G. Koontz, S.-Y. Kim, and M. J. Indelicato, "A digital reverberation simulator based on multi-port acoustic elements," *JMEST*, vol. 2, no. 1, pp. 185–191, January 2015.

[20] U. Zölzer, Ed., *Dafx: Digital Audio Effects*. New York, NY, USA: Wiley, 2002.

[21] P. Dutilleux and U. Zölzer, "Delays," in *Dafx: Digital Audio Effects*, U. Zölzer, Ed. New York, NY, USA: Wiley, 2002.

[22] ——, "Filters," in *Dafx: Digital Audio Effects*, U. Zölzer, Ed. New York, NY, USA: Wiley, 2002.

[23] T. H. Park, *Introduction to Digital Signal Processing: Computer Musically Speaking*. River Edge, NJ, USA: World Scientific, 2009.

[24] W. C. Sabine, *Collected Papers on Acoustics*. Harvard University Press, 1923.

[25] W. L. G. Koontz, "Multiport acoustic models with applications in audio signal processing," *J. Audio Eng. Soc*, vol. 61, no. 10, pp. 727–736, 2013.

[26] D. Dailey, *Electronics for Guitarists*. New York, NY, USA: Springer, 2012.

[27] W. Stanley, *Operational Amplifiers with Linear Integrated Circuits*. Upper Saddle River, NJ, USA: Pearson Education, 2002.

[28] T. Painter and A. Spanias, "Perceptual coding of digital audio," *Proceedings of the IEEE*, vol. 88, no. 4, pp. 451–515, 2000.

[29] I. O. for Standardization, *Information Technology–Coding of Moving Pictures and Associated Audio for Digital Storage Media at Up to about 1, 5 Mbit/s*. International Organization for Standardization, 1996.

[30] J. O. Smith and J. S. Abel, "Bark and erb bilinear transforms," *IEEE Transactions on Speech and Audio Processing*, vol. 7, no. 6, pp. 697–708, 1999.

[31] C. Wiesener, T. Flohrer, A. Lerch, and S. Weinzierl, "Adaptive noise reduction for real-time applications," in *Audio Engineering Society Convention 128*. Audio Engineering Society, 2010.

[32] N. Wiener, *Extrapolation, Interpolation, and Smoothing of Stationary Time Series.* Cambridge, MA, USA: MIT Press, 1964.

[33] Y. Ephraim and D. Malah, "Speech enhancement using a minimum mean-square error log-spectral amplitude estimator," *IEEE Transactions on Acoustics, Speech, and Signal Processing*, vol. 33, no. 2, pp. 443–445, 1985.

[34] I. W. Selesnickl, "Short-time Fourier transform and its inverse," *Signal*, vol. 10, no. 1, pp. 1–11, 2009.

[35] W. A. Sethares, *Rhythm and Transforms.* New York, NY, USA: Springer, 2007.

[36] U. Zölzer, *Digital Audio Signal Processing.* New York, NY, USA: Wiley, 2008.

[37] S. Zohar, "Toeplitz matrix inversion: the algorithm of W. F. Trench," *J. ACM*, vol. 16, no. 4, pp. 592–601, Oct. 1969.

[38] J. Coalson, "Flac - free lossless audio codec," July 2008, accessed July 20, 2016. [Online]. Available: https://xiph.org/flac/.

[39] R. Rice and J. Plaunt, "Adaptive variable-length coding for efficient compression of spacecraft television data," *IEEE Transactions on Communication Technology*, vol. 19, no. 6, pp. 889–897, 1971.

[40] U. Zölzer, Ed., *DAFX: Digital Audio Effects*, 2nd ed. New York, NY, USA: Wiley, 2011.

[41] P. P. Vaidyanathan, "Multirate digital filters, filter banks, polyphase networks, and applications: a tutorial," *Proceedings of the IEEE*, vol. 78, no. 1, pp. 56–93, 1990.

Index